MW00837944
Gallery of the Infinite
AMS
American Mathematical Society
Richard Evan Schwartz

2010 *Mathematics Subject Classification*. Primary 00A06, 00A30, 00A66, 00A09, 03E99

For notes on the book, including answers to the questions,
visit **www.ams.org/bookpages/mbk-97**

Library of Congress Cataloging-in-Publication Data
Names: Schwartz, Richard Evan
Title: Gallery of the Infinite / Richard Evan Schwartz.
Description: Providence, Rhode Island : American Mathematical Society, 2016. | Audience: Grade 9 to 12.- | Includes bibliographical references and index.
Identifiers: LCCN 2015033426 | ISBN 9781470425579 (alk. paper)
Subjects: LCSH: Number concept–Juvenile literature. | Arithmetic–Juvenile literature. | Infinite–Juvenile literature. | Games in mathematics education–Juvenile literature. | AMS: General – General and miscellaneous specific topics – Mathematics for nonmathematicians (engineering, social sciences, etc.). msc | General – General and miscellaneous specific topics – Philosophy of mathematics. msc | General – General and miscellaneous specific topics – Mathematics and visual arts, visualization. msc | General – General and miscellaneous specific topics – Popularization of mathematics. msc | Mathematical logic and foundations – Set theory – None of the above, but in this section. msc
Classification: LCC QA141.15 .S37 2016 | DDC 513–dc23 LC record available at http://lccn.loc.gov/2015033426

Printed in India and the United States of America.

∞ The paper used in this book is acid-free and falls within the guidelines established to ensure permanence and durability.
Visit the AMS home page at http://www.ams.org/

10 9 8 7 6 5 4 3 2 1 21 20 19 18 17 16

If you think about walking along a number line, with the numbers set out in front of you one after the other, then INFINITY...
0
1
2
3
4
5
seems to be a long way off, a point on a horizon you will never reach, a height to which you can never climb.

Infinity seems to be a thing outside of our universe ...

a far edge you won't see no
matter how hard you stare
into space.

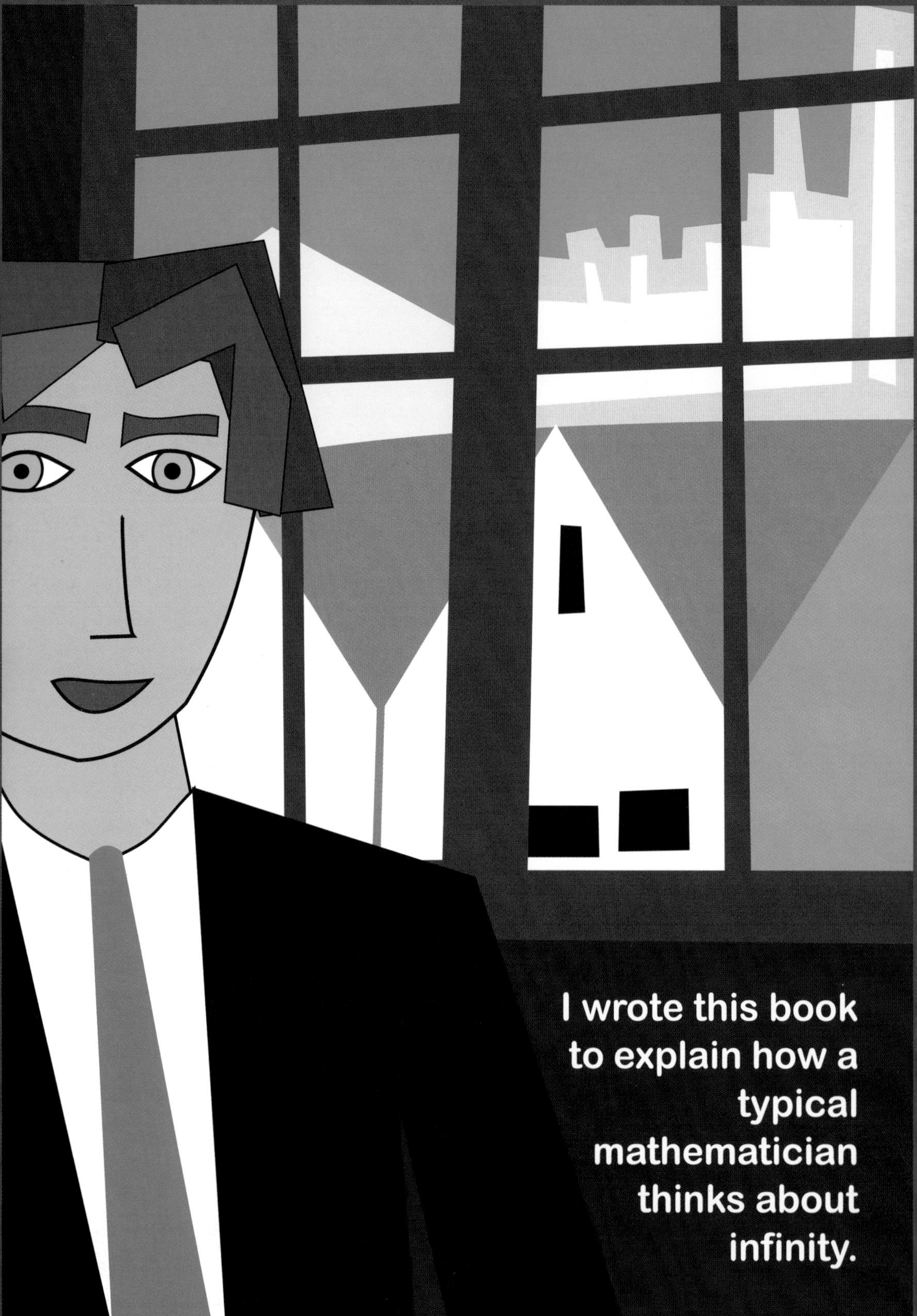

I wrote this book
to explain how a
typical
mathematician
thinks about
infinity.

The approach takes some getting used to, but you'll see that a mathematical view of infinity leads to some breathtaking surprises.

The first order of business is to talk about

SETS.

A set is the name mathematicians have for collections of things. The things in the set are called the **MEMBERS** of the set.

Traditionally, mathematicians write the members of a set in symbols, in between two brackets and separated by commas. The brackets and commas are not part of the set. They are like a frame that goes around the outside of the picture.

I sometimes picture sets as things placed inside boxes, because then the box looks more clearly like a frame.

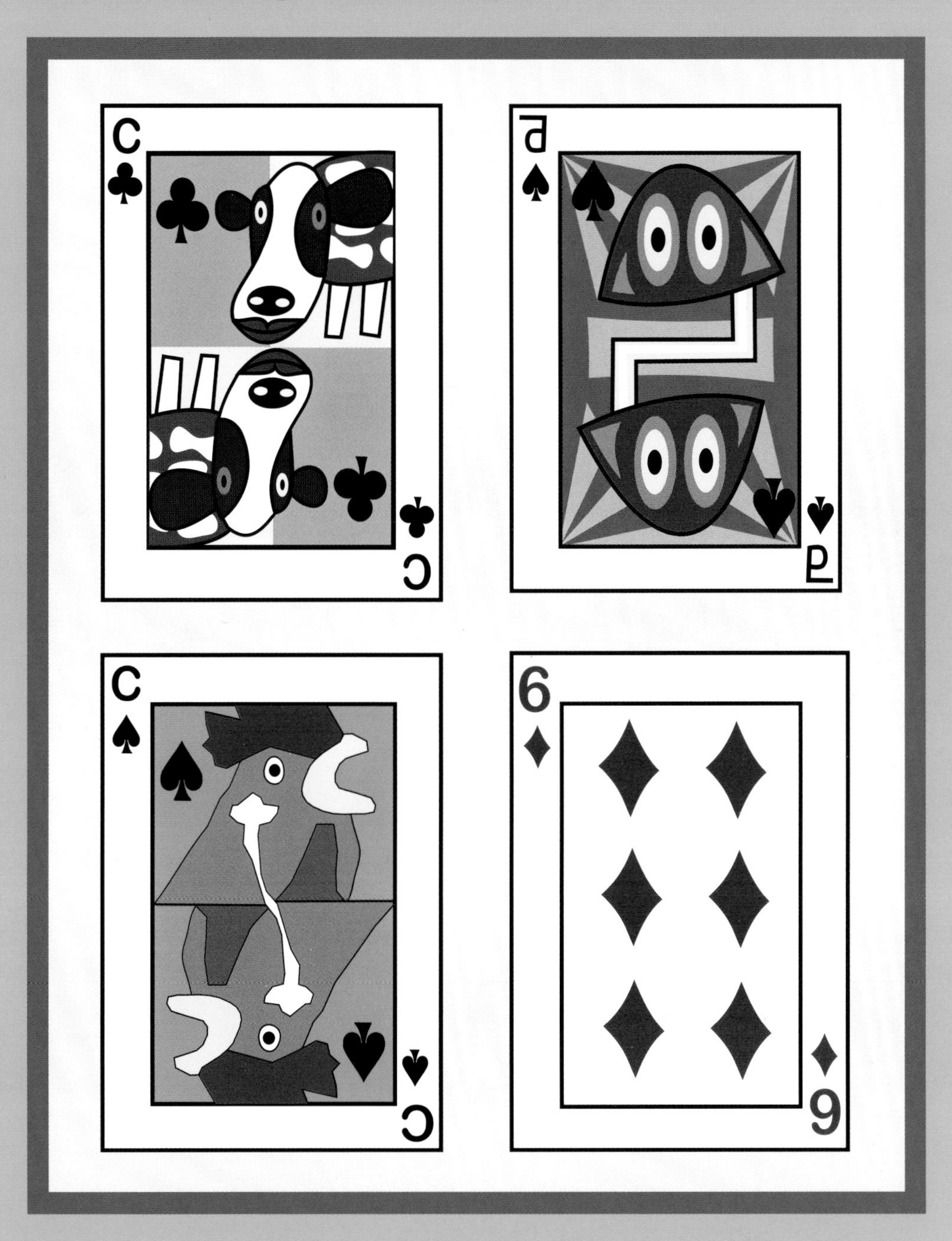

Informally, I like to picture the members of a set as all sorts of things, like playing cards...

or cats...

or aliens.

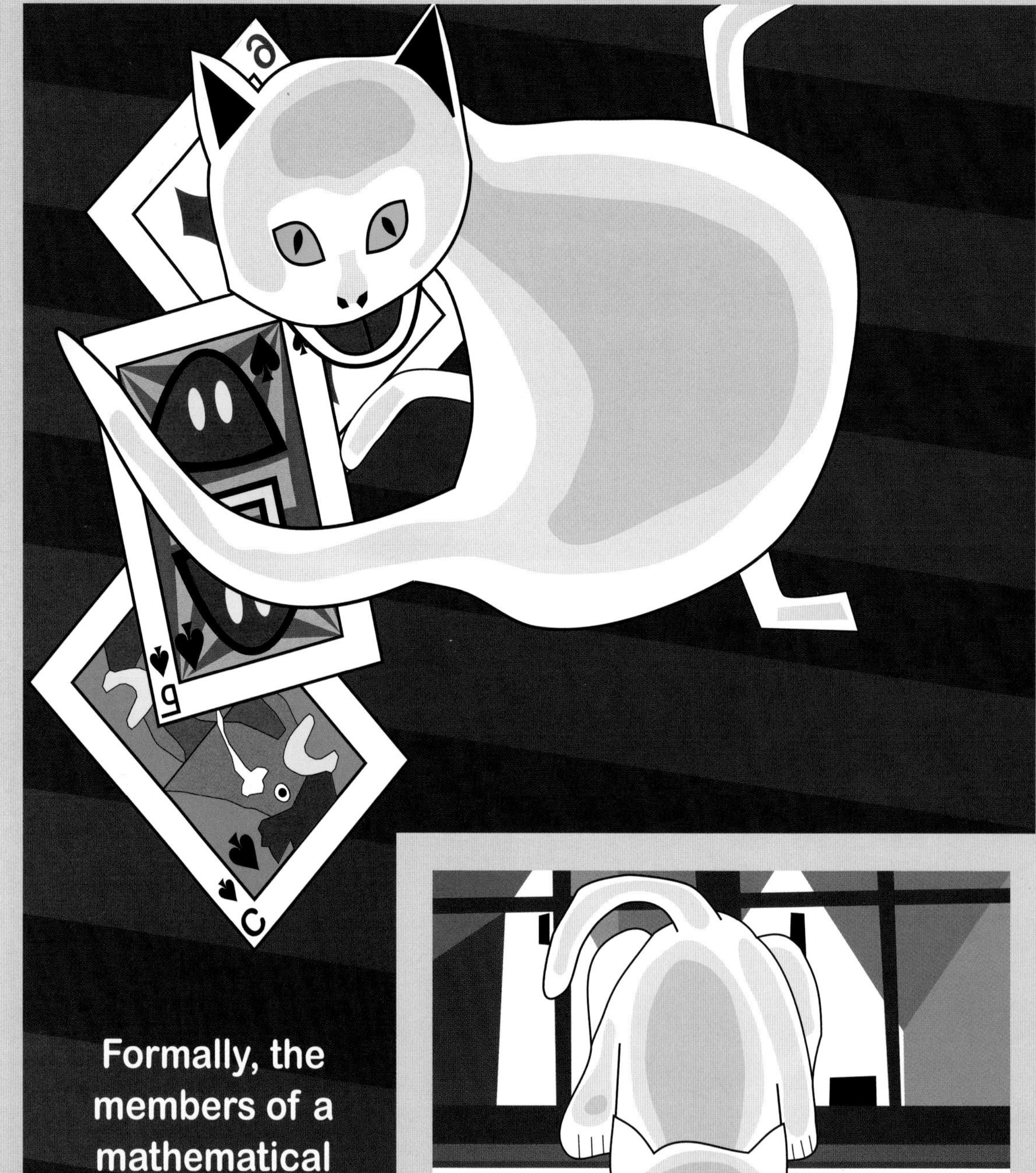
Formally, the members of a mathematical set are not really cards or cats or aliens.
They are sets themselves.

This gives mathematics a certain beauty and purity, but it does raise the question as to how the whole enterprise gets off the ground. Let's not get into these technical details just yet. For now, we'll think of sets as being all kinds of things.

Some sets are called FINITE. Here are some examples.

The set of pancake spatulas with faces drawn on them

The set of windows in Manhattan

The set of all tic-tac-toe games

The set of seagulls on the Rhode Island coast

Of course, I haven't drawn all the members of these sets.

Intuitively, a set is finite if you can start counting its members and get to the end. But this isn't phrased quite right because sometimes you might not ACTUALLY be able to get all the way to the end. Consider the set of all chess games which last less than 200 moves ...

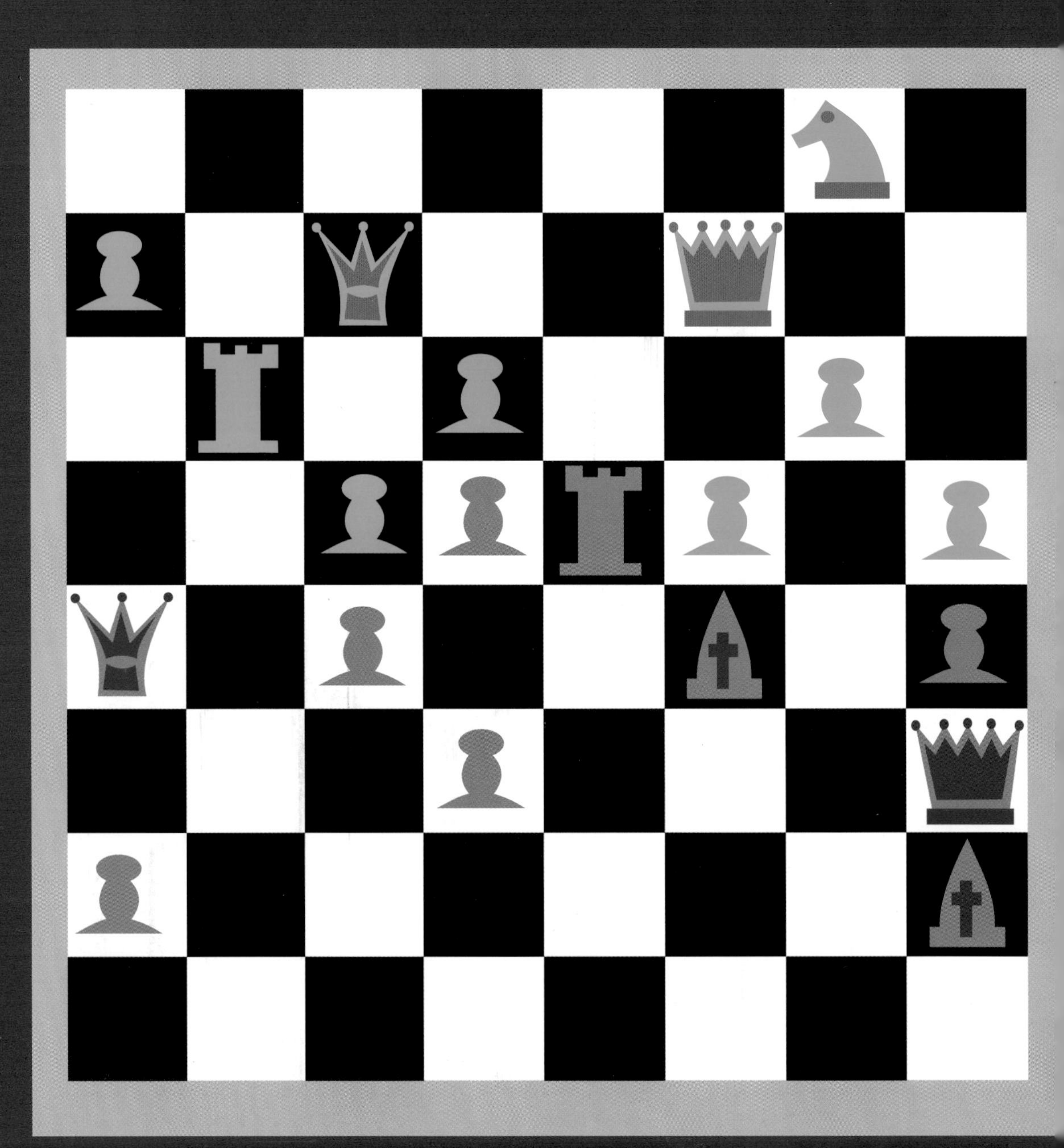

or the set of all molecules on Earth. It is hard give a formal definition of a finite set, but we certainly seem to recognize finite sets when we see them.

Incidentally, one of these sets has WAY more members than the other. Which one?

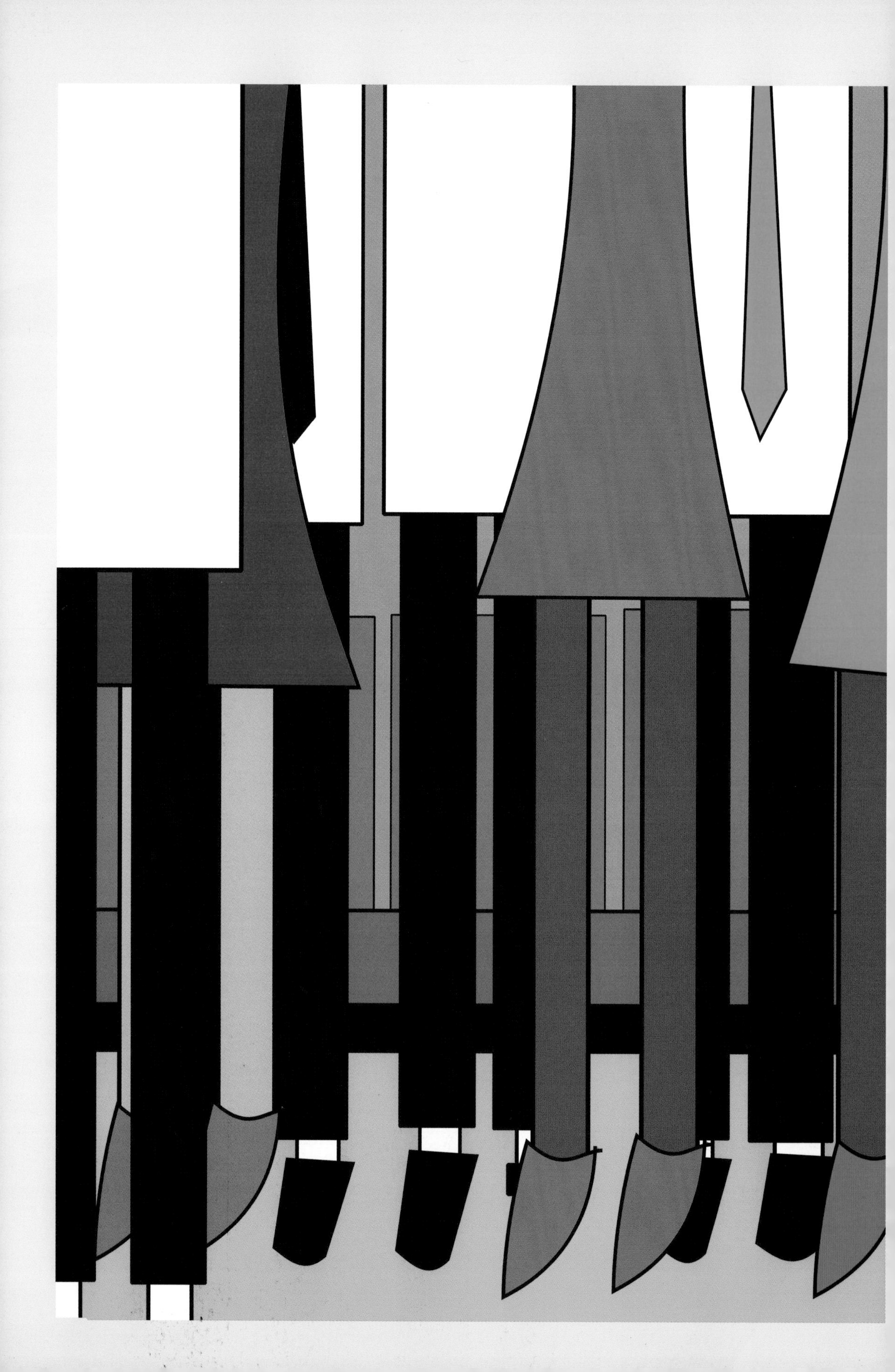

Sometimes you might want to compare sets without having to count them. Are there more people or chairs at a concert? Just have everyone pick a chair and sit down. See if you have extra chairs or extra people, or if there is a perfect match.

Are there more children or gumballs?

It would be crazy to count! Just give each kid a gumball and see if there are kids left over at the end, or gumballs.

When two sets match up perfectly, the matching between them is known as a

BIJECTION.

Here is a bijection between a set of cats and a set of cards.

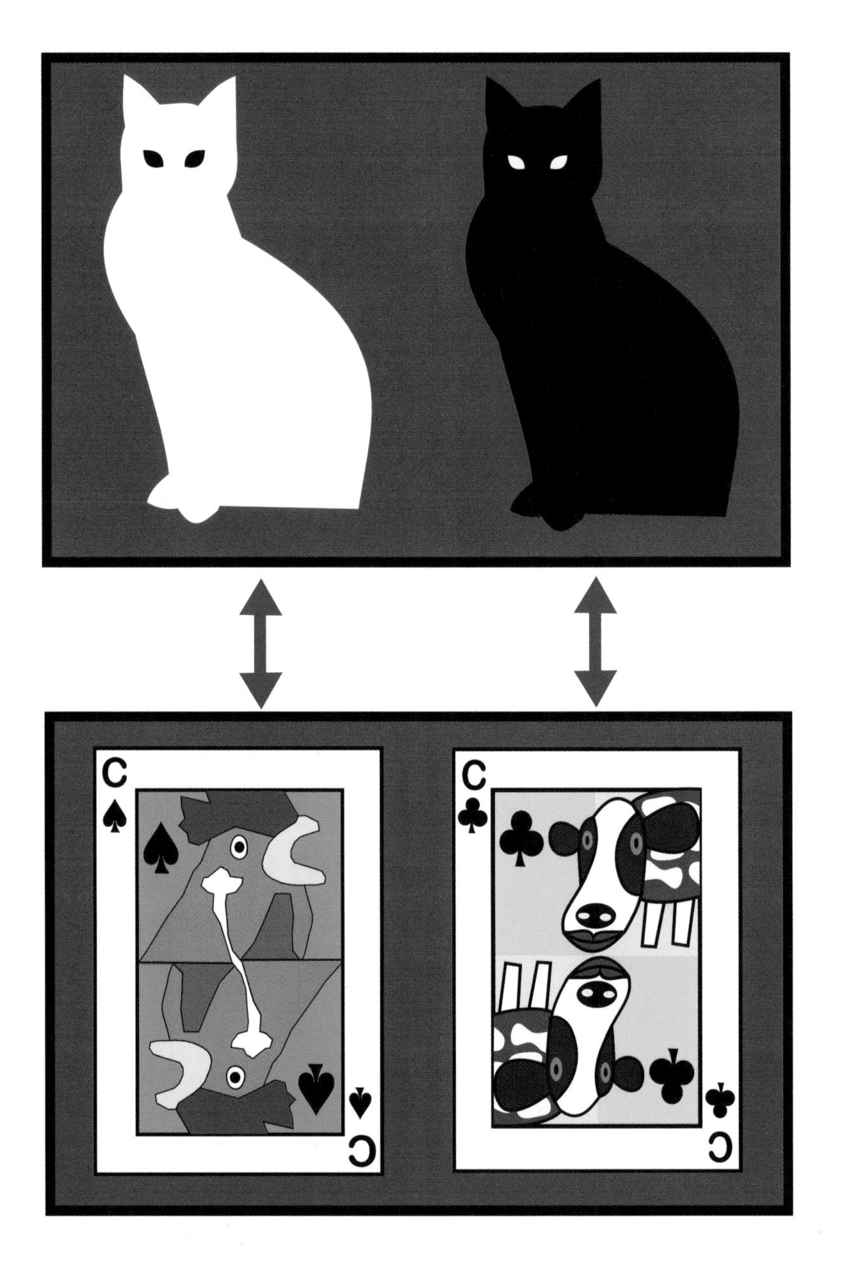

In a bijection, different members of one set are matched with different members of the other, and nothing is left over.
If both cats got matched to the chicken, they might fight over it.

Here is one of the many bijections between the set {A,B,C,D,E,F,G,H,I,J,K,L} and the set of hours on a clock...

and here are a few others.

This bijection might remind you of binary numbers.

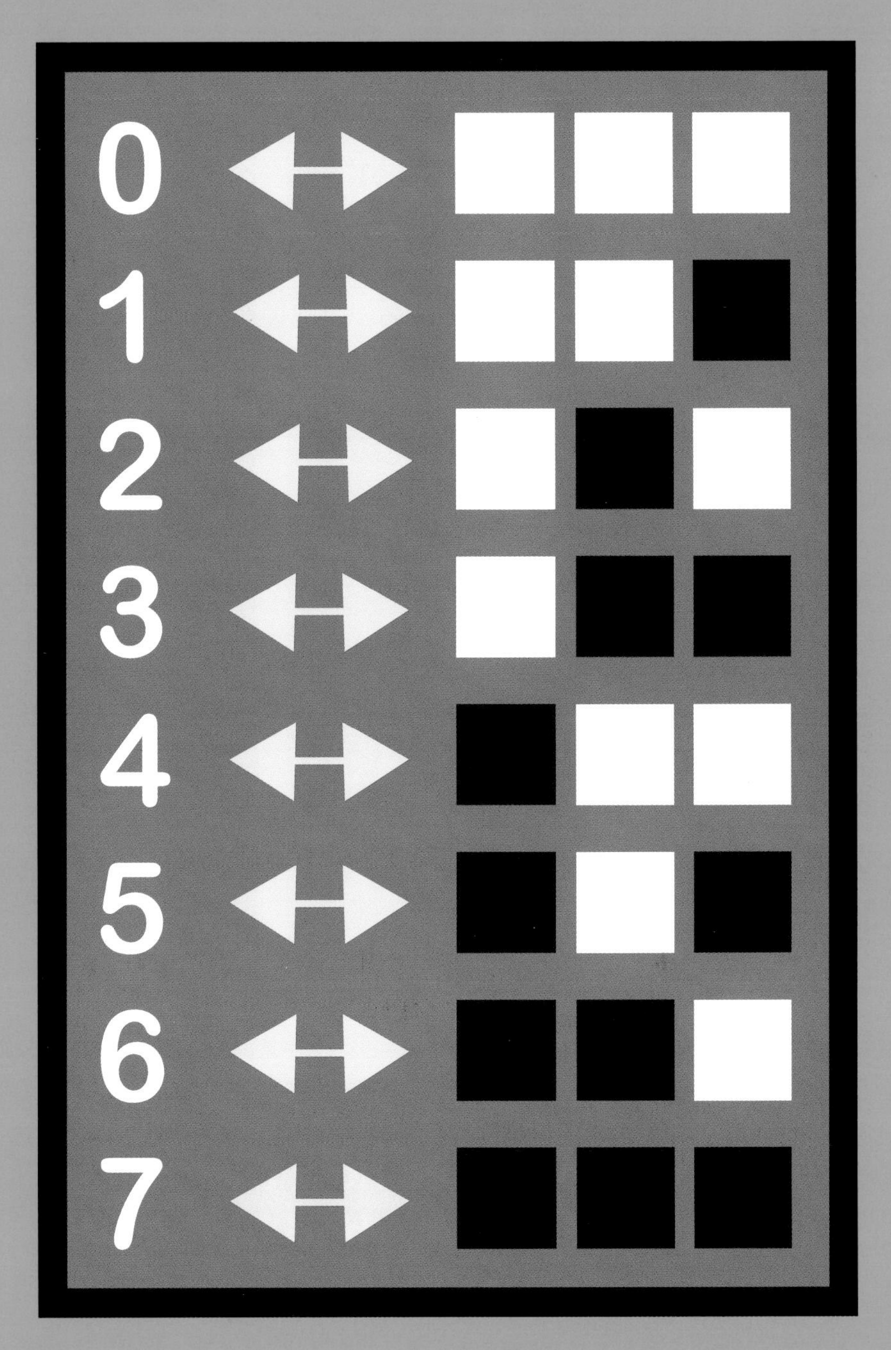

Finding a bijection between two finite sets is a way of saying that they have the same size.

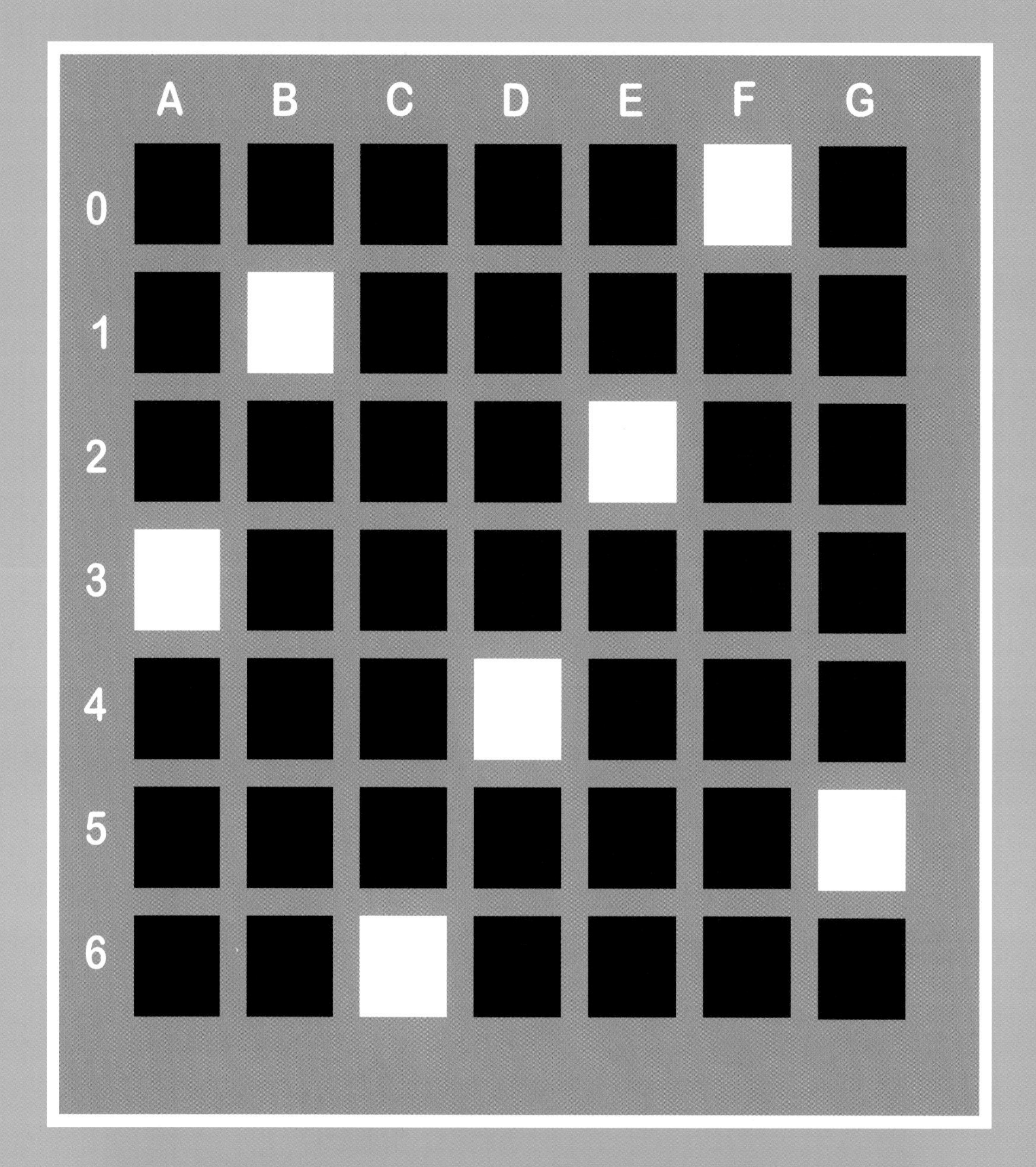

This chart illustrates how the set {0,1,2,3,4,5,6} is matched to the set {A,B,C,D,E,F,G}. You can read from the chart that 0 is matched to F and 1 is matched to B, and so on.

Here are a few more of the 5040 possible bijections between these two sets.

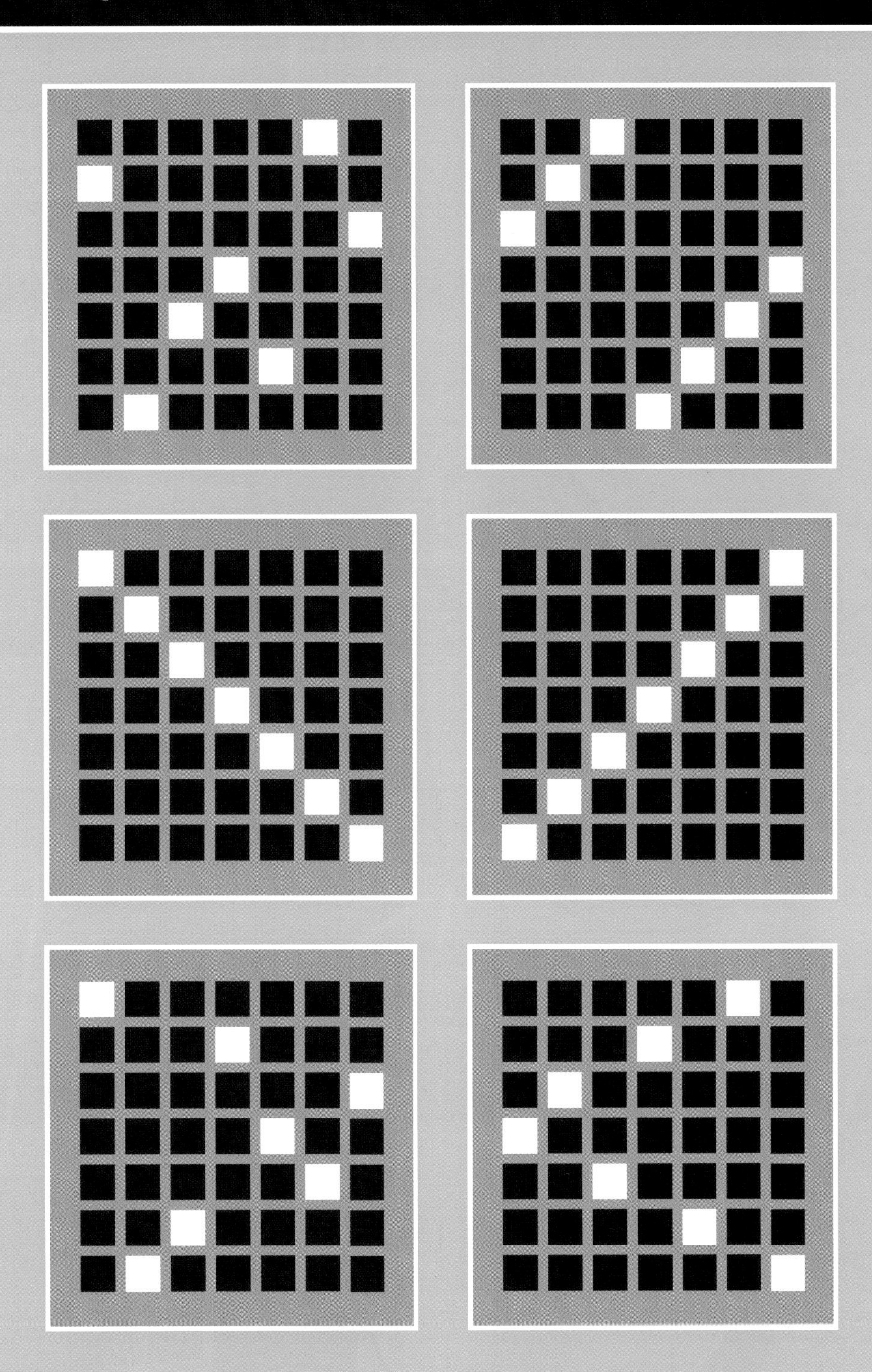

As one last example, there is a bijection between the set of animal bodies and and the set of their heads.

**Let us talk more about sets.
If the members of sets are sets themselves, how does the whole enterprise get off the ground?**

You could say that the whole theory of sets is founded on the existence of

NOTHING.

It is one thing to say that nothing exists and quite another to say that

NOTHING

exists. I sometimes imagine NOTHING as a blank red painting hanging in an art gallery that nobody visits.

The mathematical concept for NOTHING is the empty set:

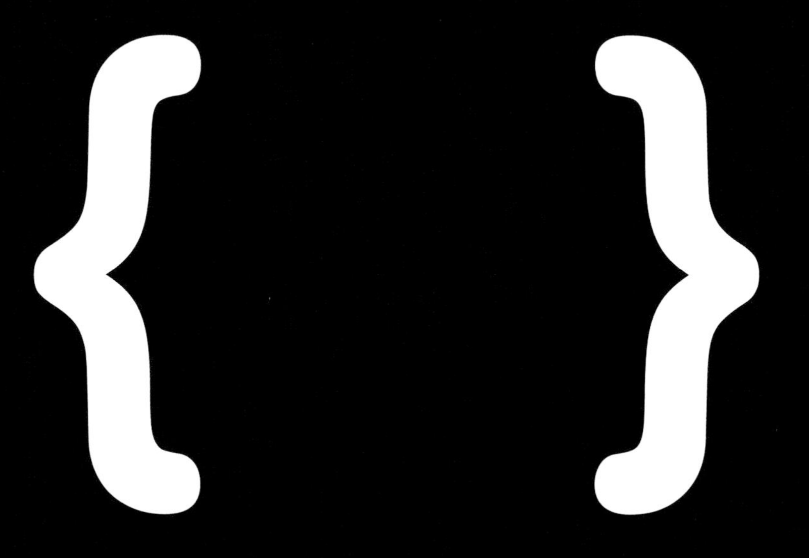

It is the set with no members.

Once we have the empty set, we can form the set whose only member is the empty set.

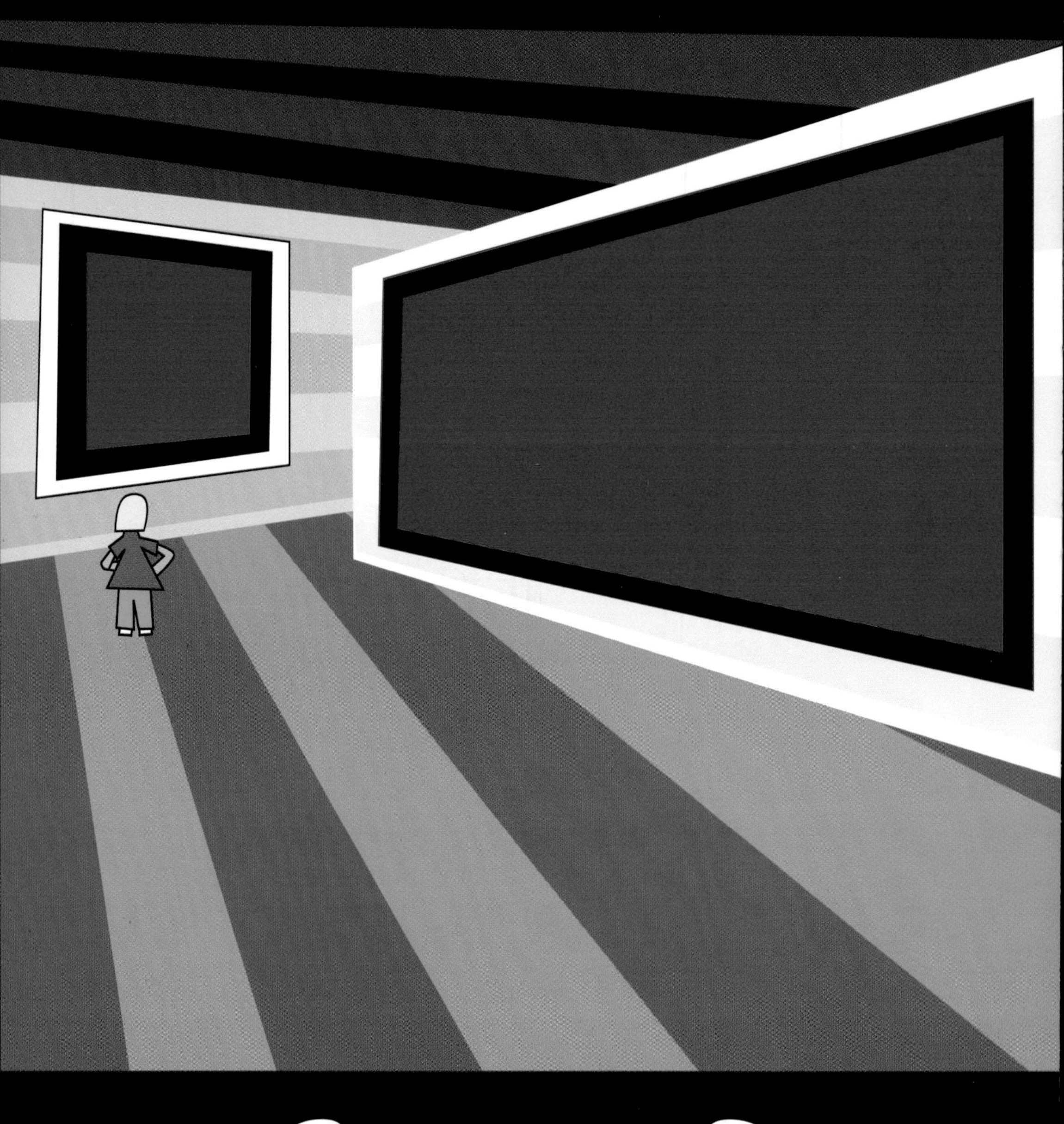

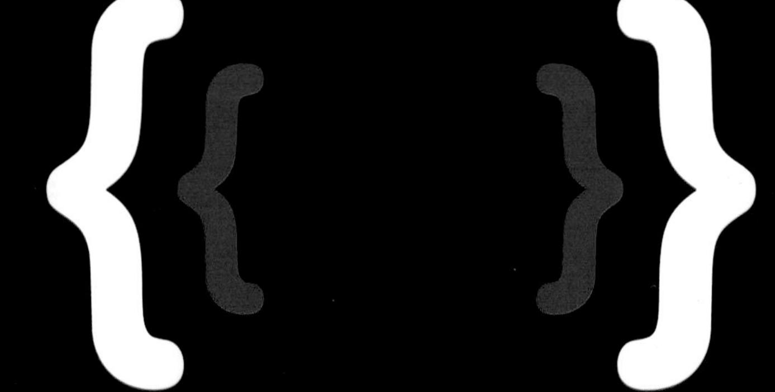

Next, we can form the set whose members
are the empty set and the set whose
member is the emptyset.
{{ }, {{ }}}

Next ...

...and so on. Now I want to say a word about how we can define numbers in terms of these sets.

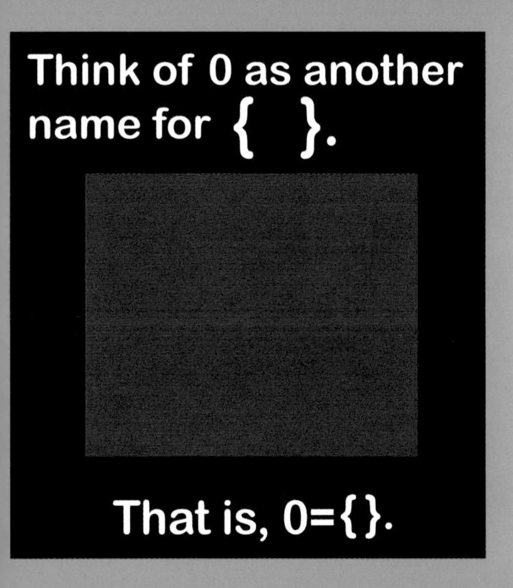

Think of 0 as another name for { }.

That is, 0={ }.

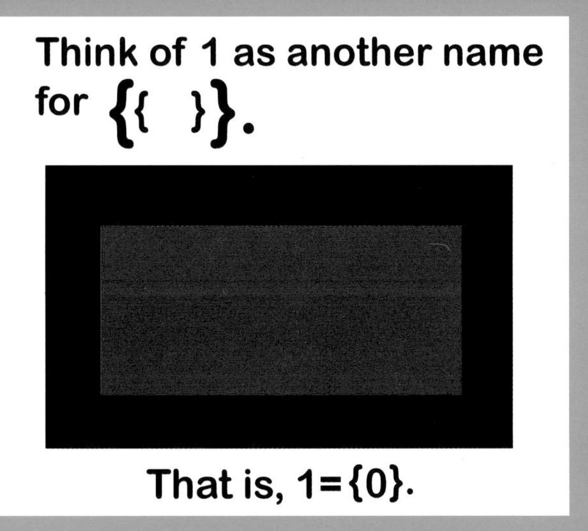

Think of 1 as another name for {{ }}.

That is, 1={0}.

Think of 2 as another name for

{{ },{{ }}}.

That is, 2={0,1}.

The pattern continues:
3={{ },{{ }},{{ },{{ }}}={0,1,2}, etc.
From this point of view, numbers are just organized emptiness!

At the risk of sounding a bit strange, let me confess something about my view of the world. Sometimes I think that everything is just organized emptiness.

Consider a baby.

Organic material turns out to be highly organized chains of atoms, which we often picture as patterns of balls and rods.

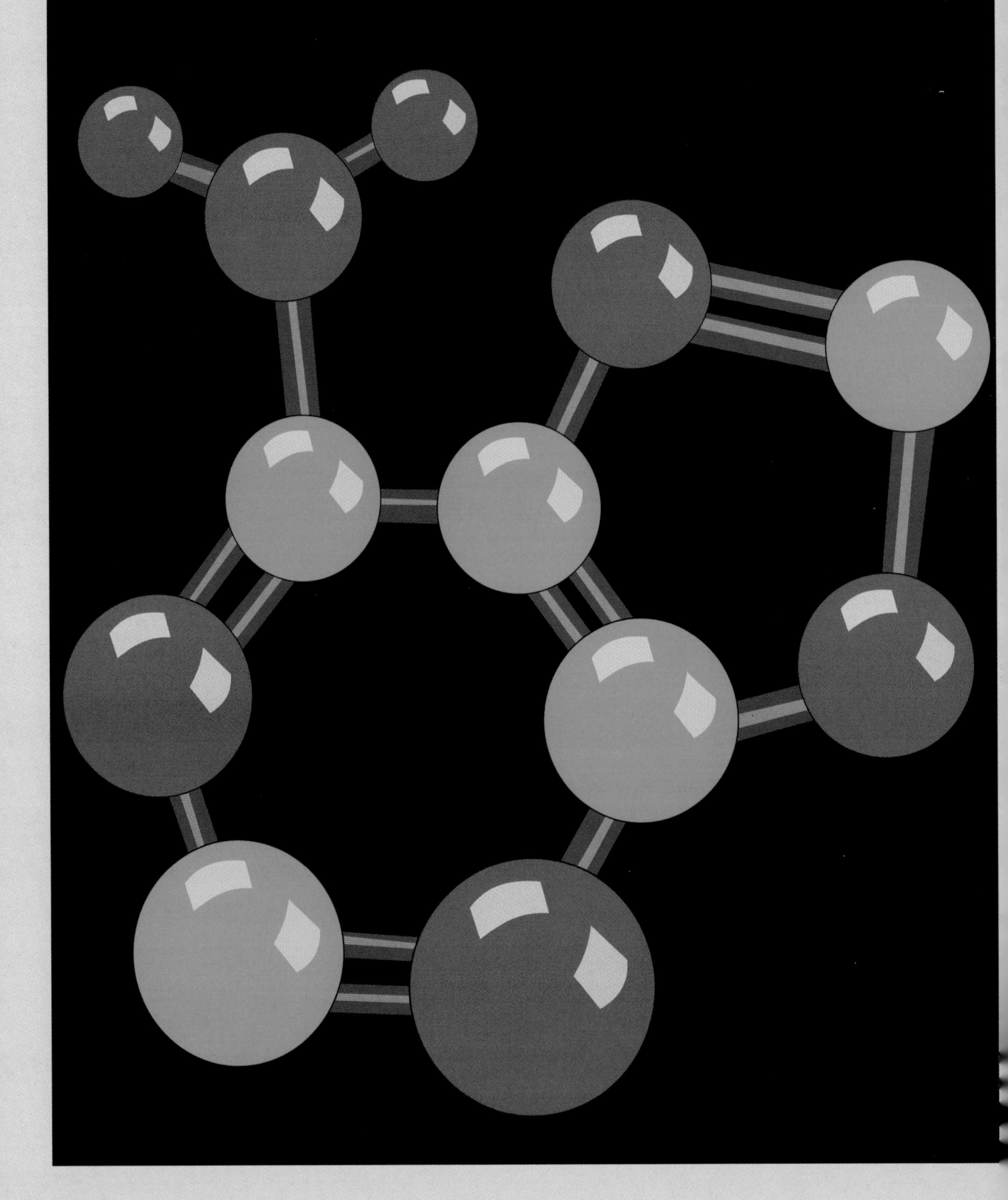

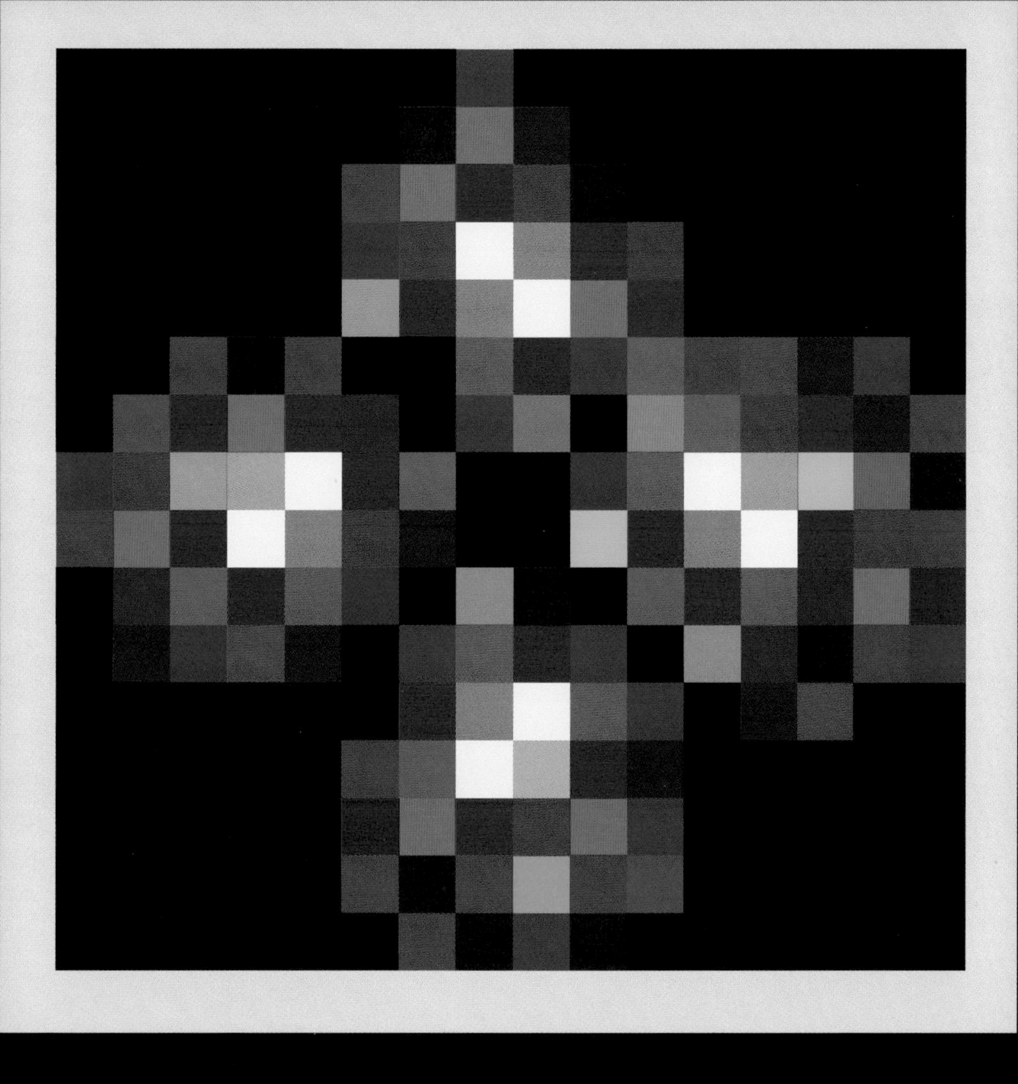

The "balls" are mostly empty space, tiny protons and neutrons surrounded by a cloud of electrons. The "rods" are shared electron clouds. The clouds are described by the same language that mathematicians invented to understand music. At this scale, physical reality blends into pure mathematics.

At still smaller scales we have no experience of physical reality at all. We just have mathematical models we invented to predict the outcomes of experiments. Sometimes there aren't even experiments to go along with the models, and we like them purely on mathematical grounds.

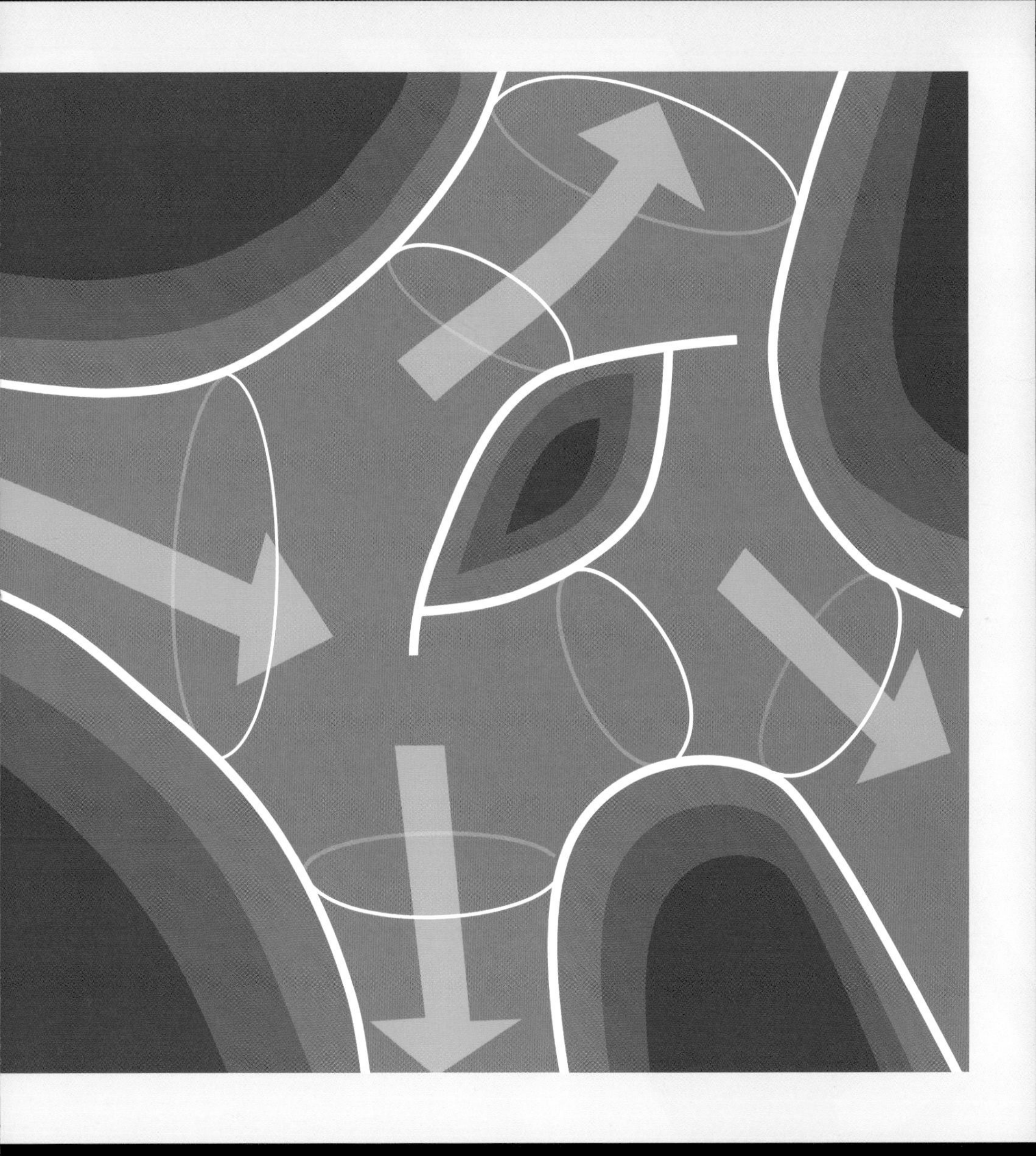

Like numbers, these models can be expressed in terms of sets.

Ultimately, our models of reality boil down to complicated patterns involving the empty set.

If you think about it in a certain way,
there isn't such a huge difference between
things in the real world and sets.

They're both part of a grand fugue composed of logic and silence.

But I digress.

Whether or not you think of everyday objects as sets it is useful for the purpose of illustration to speak of sets as if their members were all kinds of things.

Now then, a set is called
INFINITE
if it is not finite.

To a mathematician, "infinity" isn't one thing. There are finite sets and infinite sets. "Being infinite" is a property that a set may have.

The question is:
Are there infinite sets?

I'll give you two answers,
one now and one later.

Yes, of course there are!
There are lots and lots of
infinite sets.

The most famous
infinite set is
known as
$\aleph_0$.

$\aleph_0$ is the set of all counting numbers, namely {0,1,2,3,...}. It is pronounced "Aleph Nought". Aleph is the first letter in the Hebrew alphabet.

Think about $\aleph_0$ like this.
You and your friends
are in line to see the
gallery of finite
numbers.

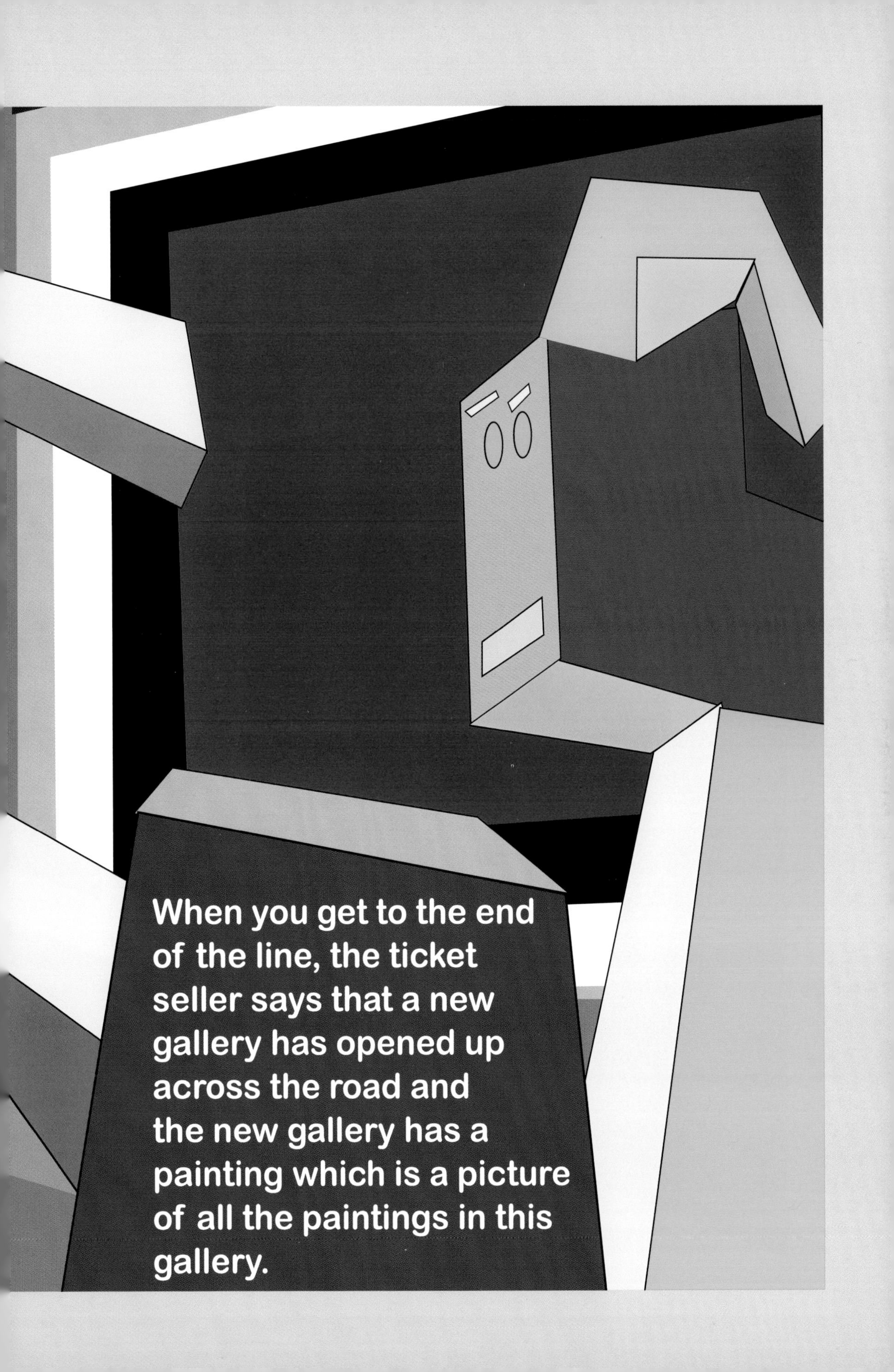
When you get to the end of the line, the ticket seller says that a new gallery has opened up across the road and the new gallery has a painting which is a picture of all the paintings in this gallery.

Here is the painting of $\aleph_0$.

There are plenty of infinite sets besides $\aleph_0$. Consider the set of even counting numbers: {0,2,4,...}. Even though chickens don't have teeth, I like to picture {0,2,4,...} as the set of teeth on an infinite chicken who has lost every other tooth. It might appear that {0,2,4,...} is somehow smaller than $\aleph_0$ because, after all ...

teeth are missing!

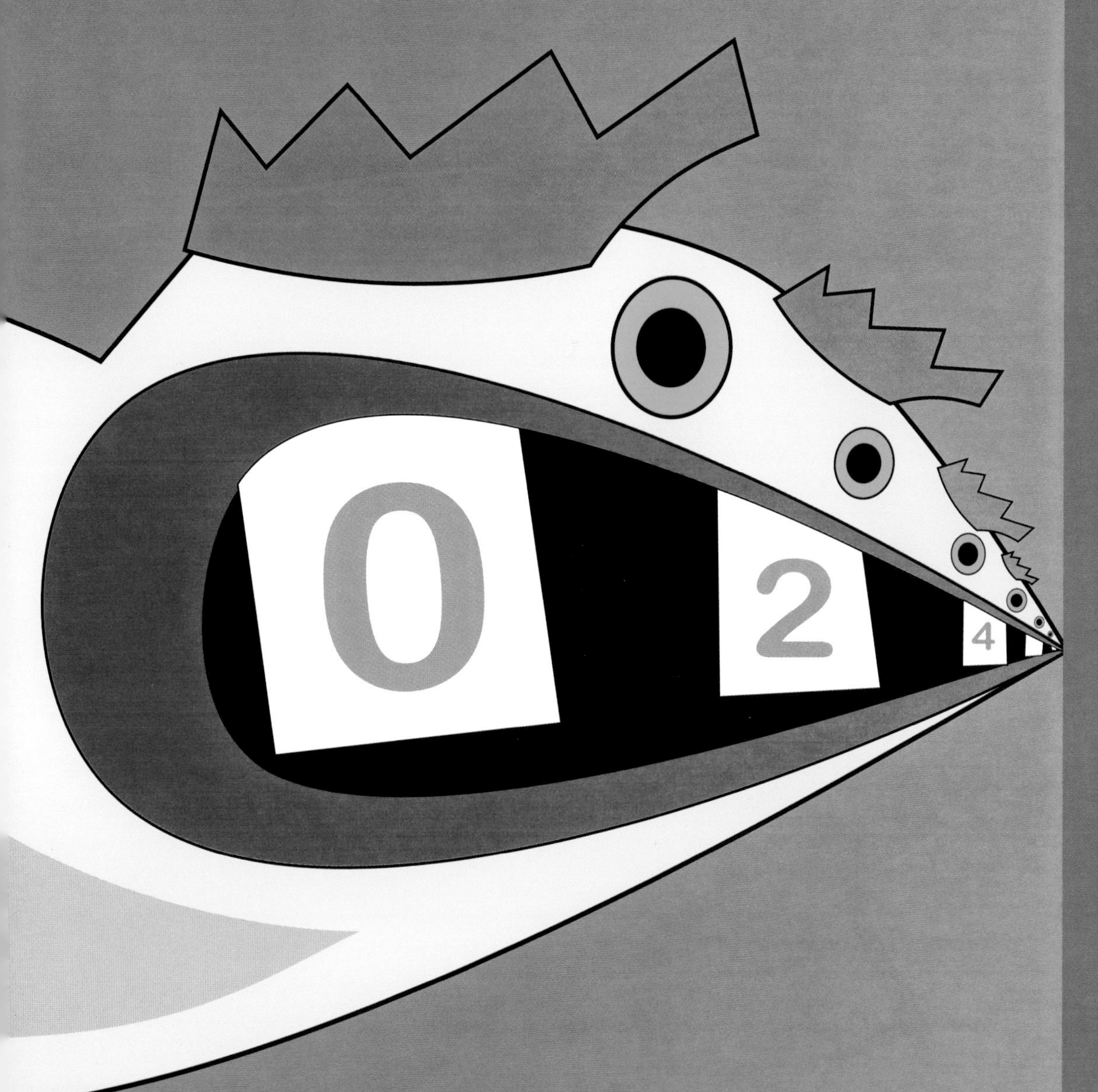

On the other hand ...

imagine that our chicken gets braces,
and after a few hellish years...

the braces pull his teeth together.

The "amount" of
teeth hasn't changed
because the teeth have just
slid around, but now it seems that
the set of chicken's teeth is the same as $\aleph_0$.

With profound insight,
Georg Cantor (1845–1918)
found a way out of these
seeming paradoxes.

Taking inspiration from the
way things work out for
finite sets, Cantor introduced
the fundamental idea that ...

two sets are the
the same size precisely
when there is a
bijection between them.

What Cantor did was extend the concept of size ...
from the realm of the finite to the realm of the infinite.

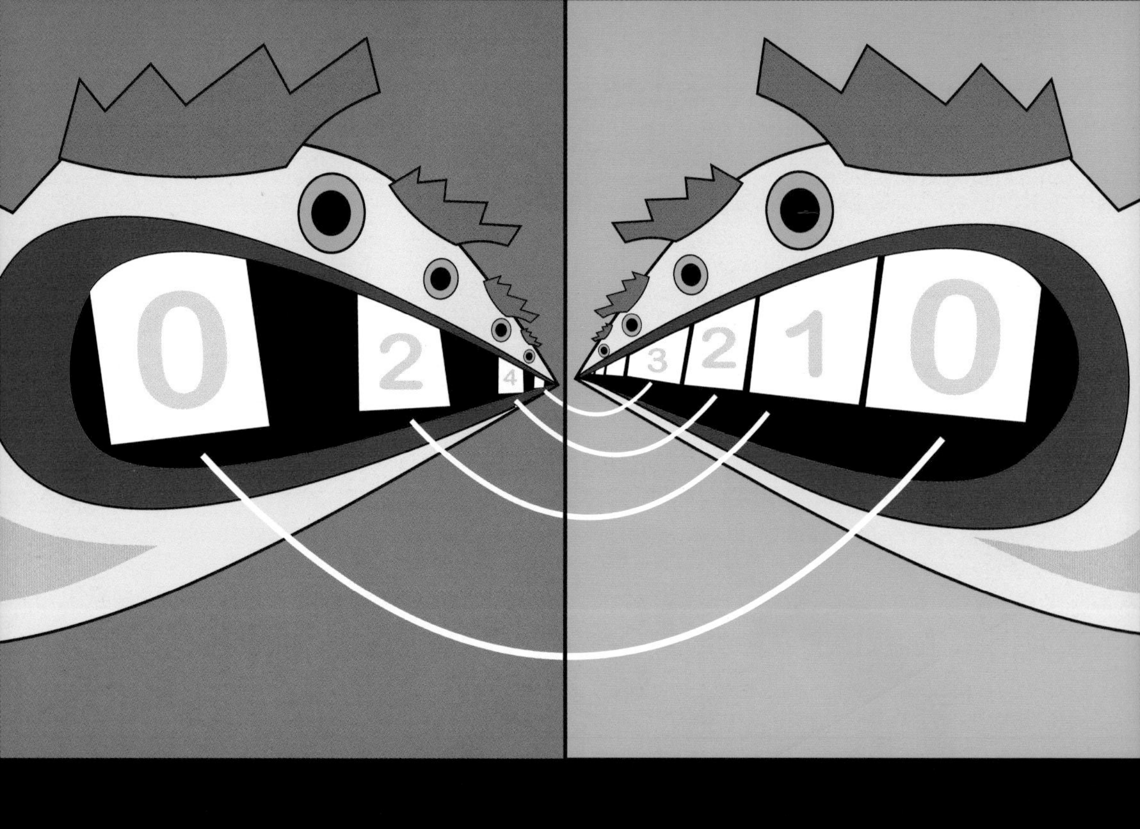

Going back to our long-suffering infinite chicken, we see that the motion of the braces produces a bijection between the set of even counting numbers and the set of all counting numbers. So, according to Cantor's definition, these two sets have the same size.

The argument works the same way for any infinite set of counting numbers. Just put on the braces and let the teeth

Cantor's definition has a nice feature:
If two sets are the same size as a third,
then they are the same size as each other.
This leads me to the Chicken Principle:

If a set has the same size as an infinite
set of counting numbers, then the set
has the same size as $\aleph_0$.

The Chicken Principle has other names,
but I like to call it the Chicken Principle.

What about other infinite sets?

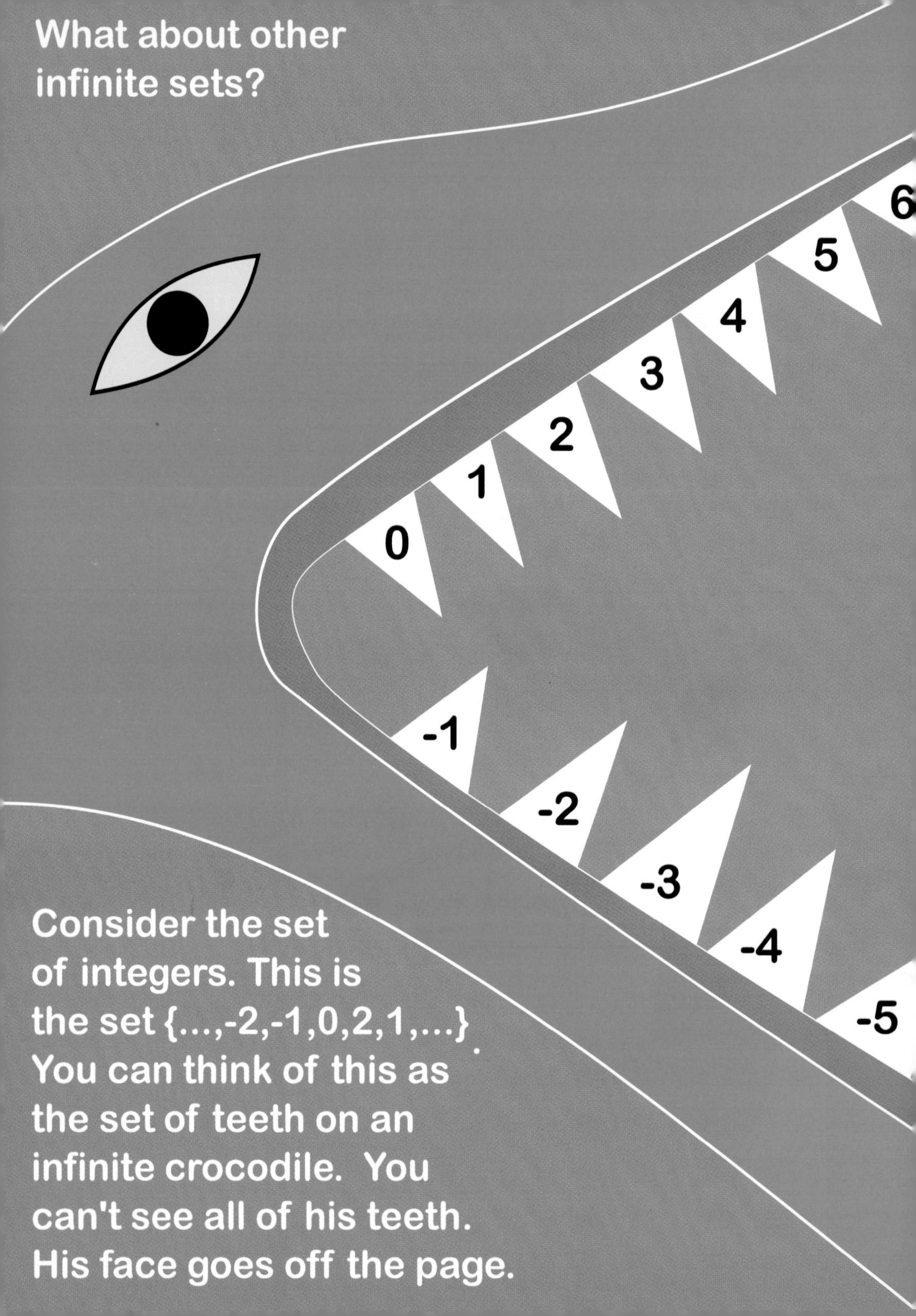

Consider the set of integers. This is the set {...,-2,-1,0,2,1,...}. You can think of this as the set of teeth on an infinite crocodile. You can't see all of his teeth. His face goes off the page.

At first it might seem that the set of integers has a larger size than $\aleph_0$. But look what happens when this guy closes his mouth.

The teeth line up, and you can see that there is a bijection between the set of integers and $\aleph_0$.

Consider an infinite rational shark.

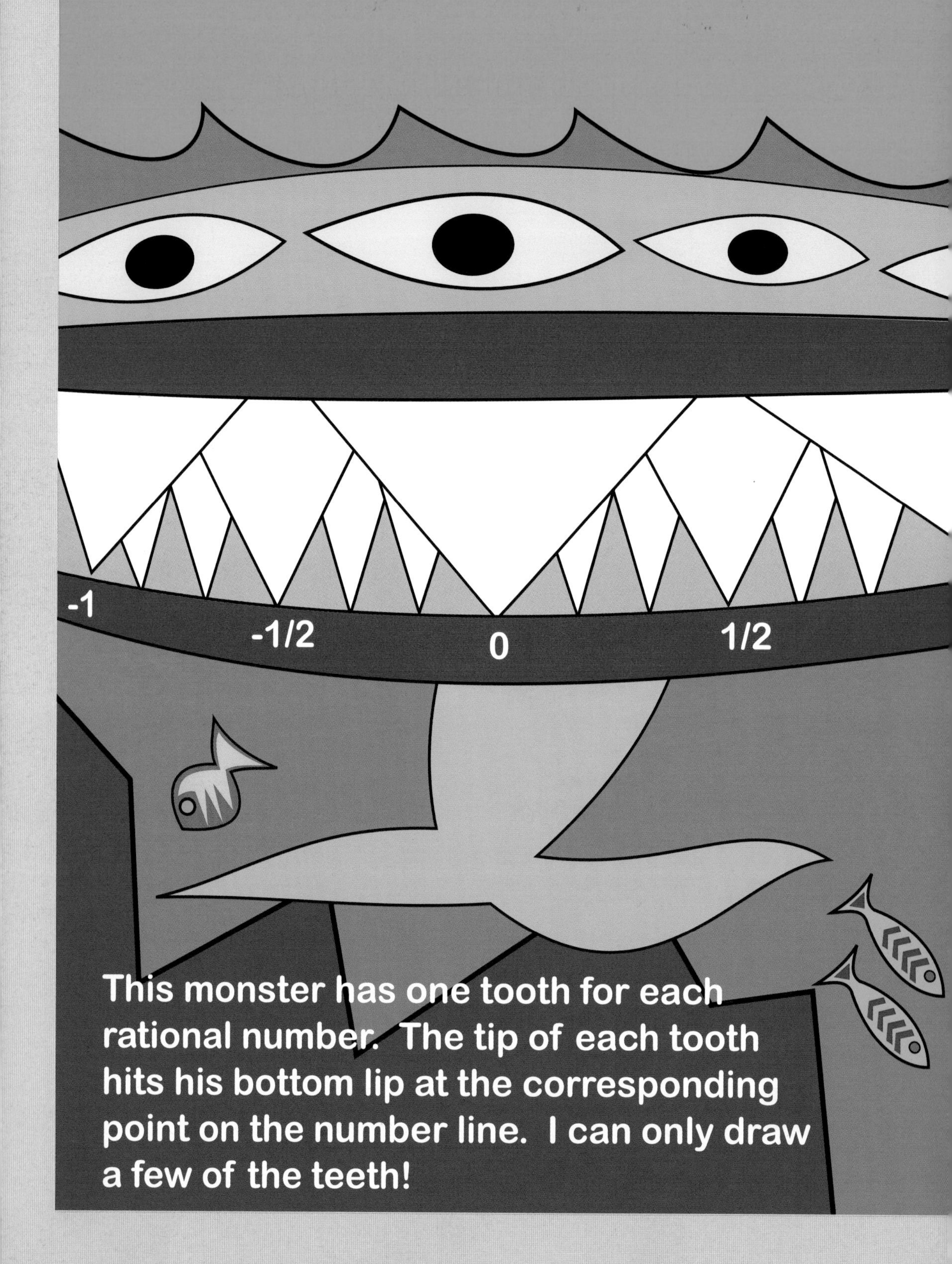
-1
-1/2
0
1/2
This monster has one tooth for each rational number. The tip of each tooth hits his bottom lip at the corresponding point on the number line. I can only draw a few of the teeth!

It seems that the shark has way more than $\aleph_0$ teeth. The teeth are everywhere! But here is a proof that the set of rational numbers has the same size as $\aleph_0$.

Step 1:

Use an infinite spiral path to create a bijection between an infinite grid of squares to $\aleph_0$. As the picture suggests, 0 is matched with the middle square, then 1 is matched with the square just to the right, and so on.

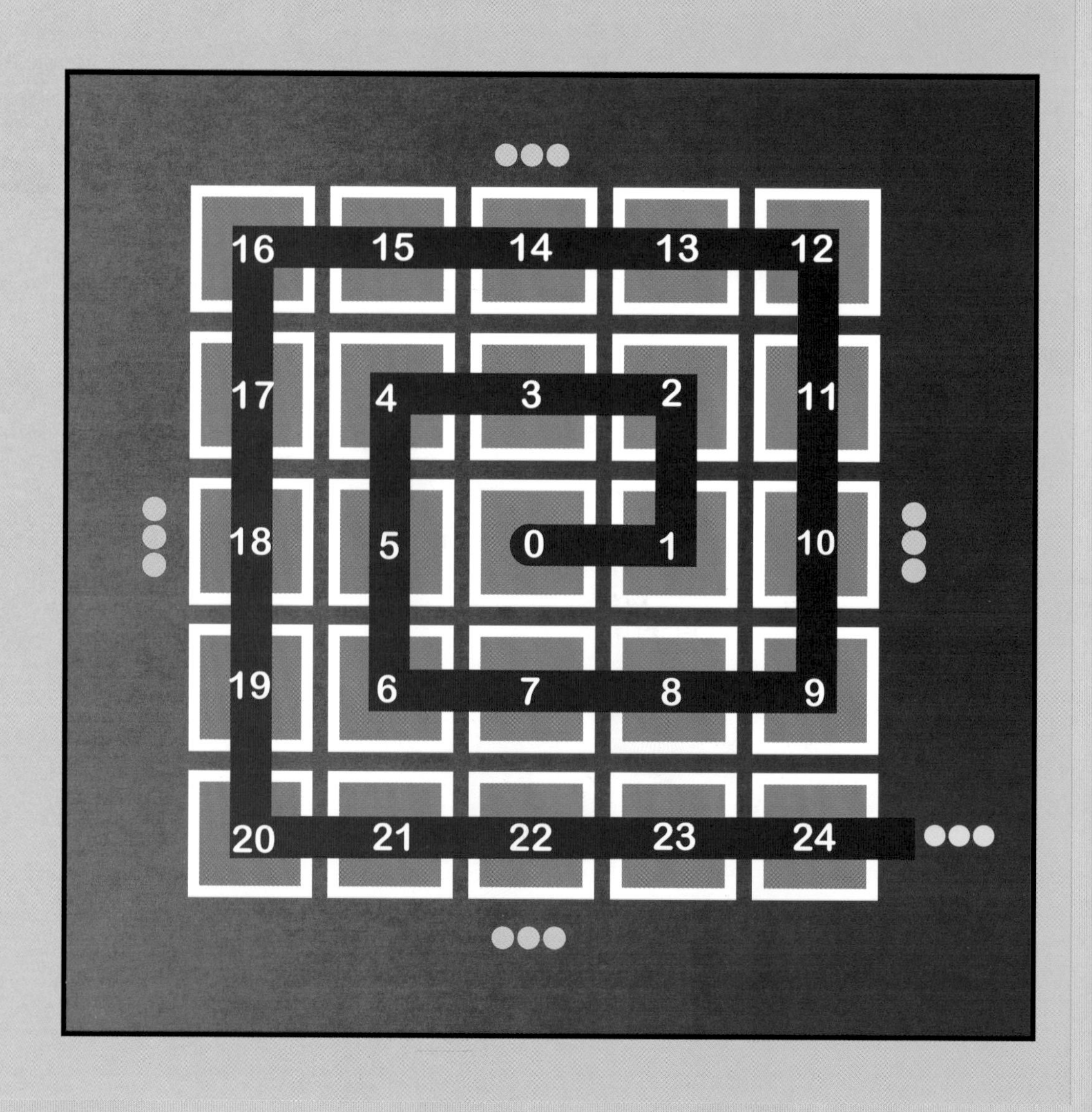

Step 2:

Label the grid like this, so that every rational number appears somewhere in it. The method shown also produces some junk, like 1/0, but that is OK.

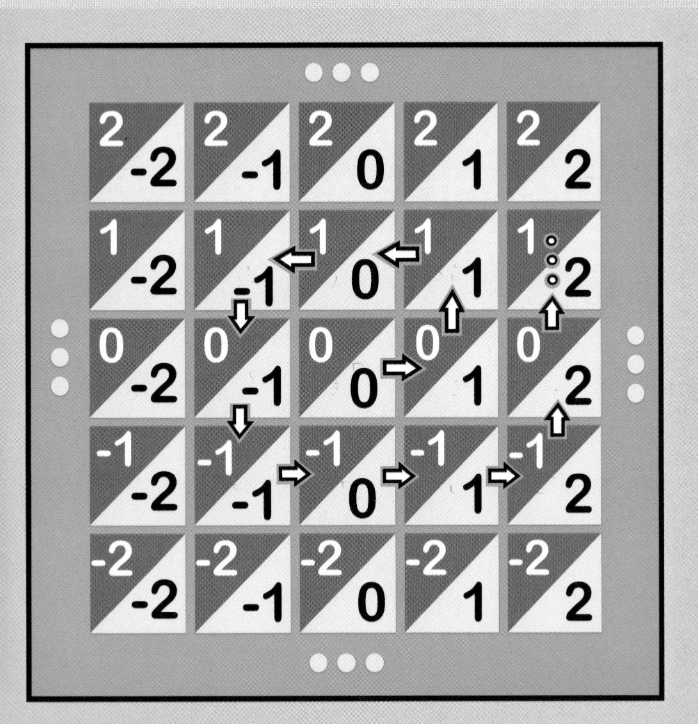

Step 3:

Move along the spiral path and make a list of the labels you see.

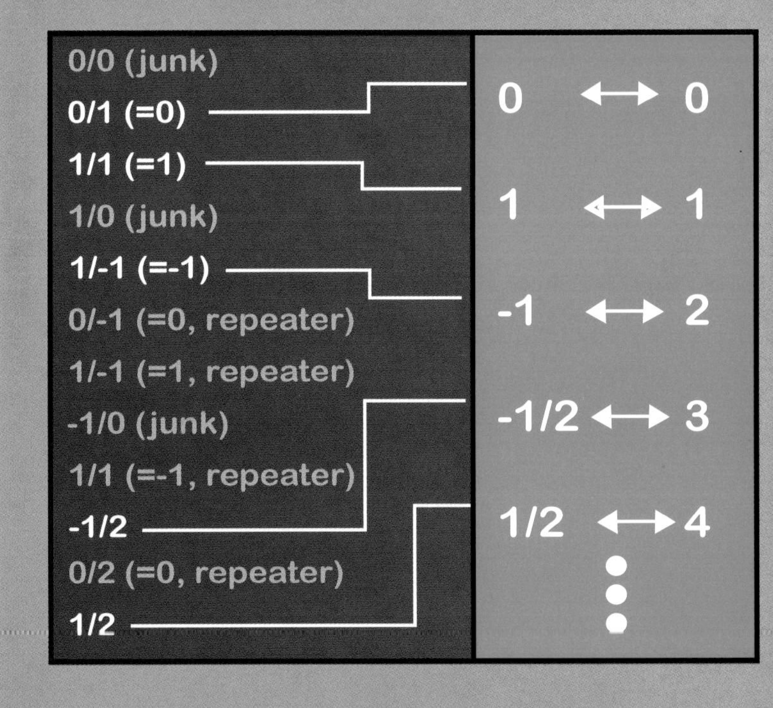

Step 4:

Remove the junk and repeaters. This gives the bijection.

I can't resist giving one more example. Consider the set of all finite text messages. For each message:

333333333 3 3333333333333

I 1 A 2 M

9 1 13

1. Place a 1 between each word.
2. Place a 2 between each letter.
3. Place a string of 3s above each letter, according to the "position" of the letter.
4. String the numbers together:

3333333331323333333333333

This way of encoding text messages matches the set of all text messages with an infinite set of counting numbers. So, the Chicken Principle says that the set of finite text messages has the same size as $\aleph_0$.

As an afterthought, I want to point out that you can communicate every rational number as a finite text message.

-2/7

minus two over seven

So, this method gives a second way to match up the set of rational numbers with an infinite set of counting numbers.

The curator of the infinite gallery
is extremely picky.
Have a
nice day!

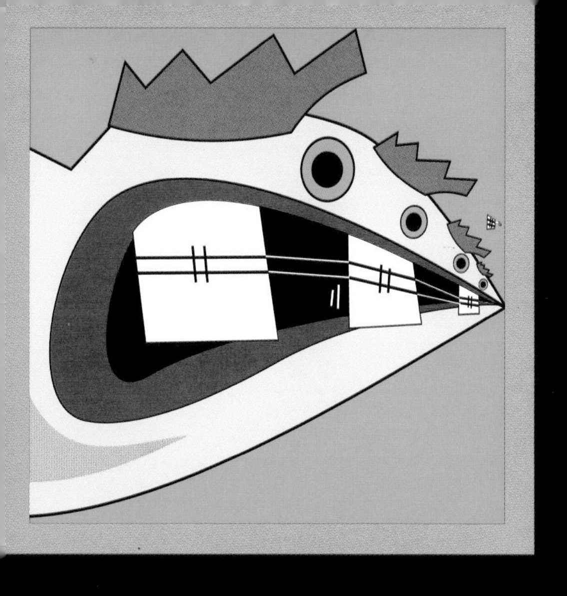

She doesn't want any duplication. She's not going to display a new painting if the set it depicts is the same size as one she already has. She heartlessly rejects all these $\aleph_0$ knockoffs. So, you may then ask ...

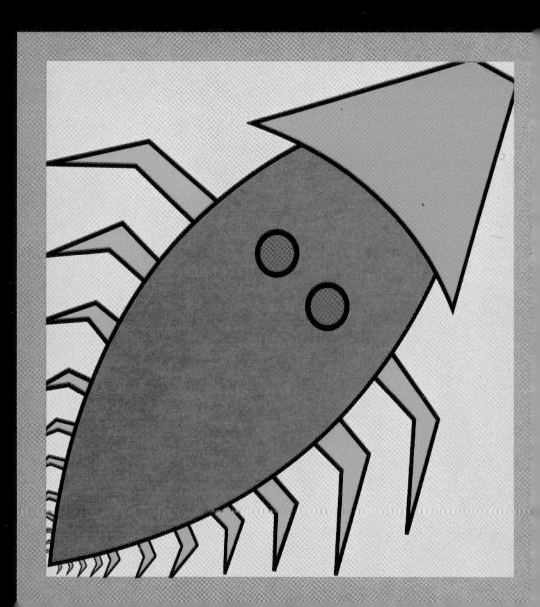

what

ELSE

is in the
infinite
gallery?

Perhaps the infinite gallery only has one painting in it! That is, maybe all infinite sets have the same size. You, my friend, are now ready for ...

the
famous...

Cantor diagonal argument.

A BINARY STRING

is a way of coloring the counting numbers black or white. You can picture an infinite row of colored boxes:

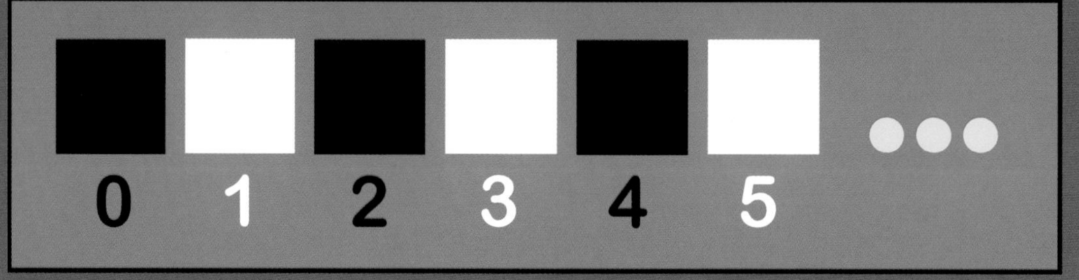

I can't draw the whole thing for you, but this example is meant to suggest that the even numbers are colored black and the odd ones white. Of course, there might not be any pattern at all in a binary string.

$$2^{\aleph_0}$$

is the name of the set of all binary strings.

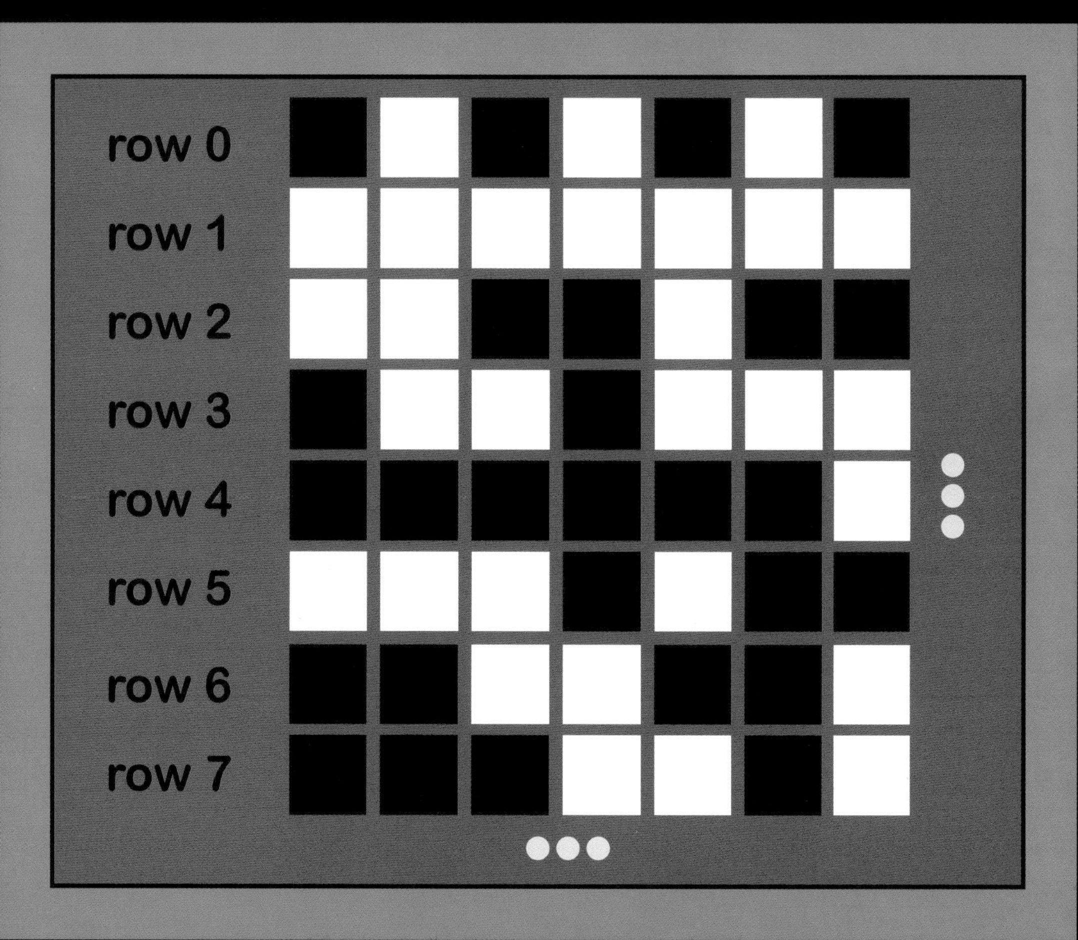

If the answer were yes, then we could record the bijection in a chart like the one here. Row 0 shows the binary string matched to 0, and so on. I can't draw the whole thing, of course, but ...

every binary string appears on some row of the chart.

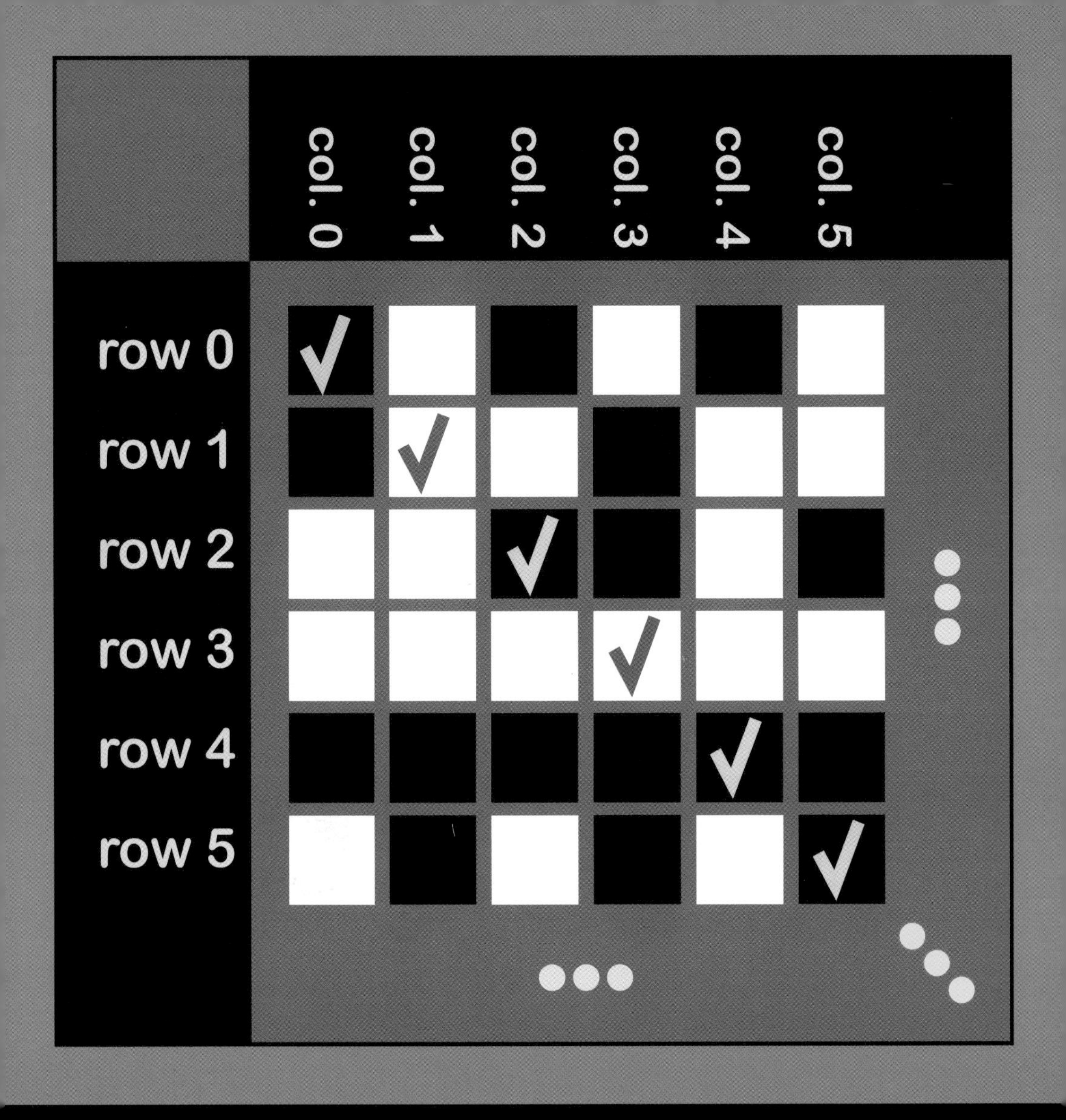

Imagine walking down the diagonal of the chart and recording the colors you see:

Reverse all the colors on the diagonal string, and call the new string "Bob".

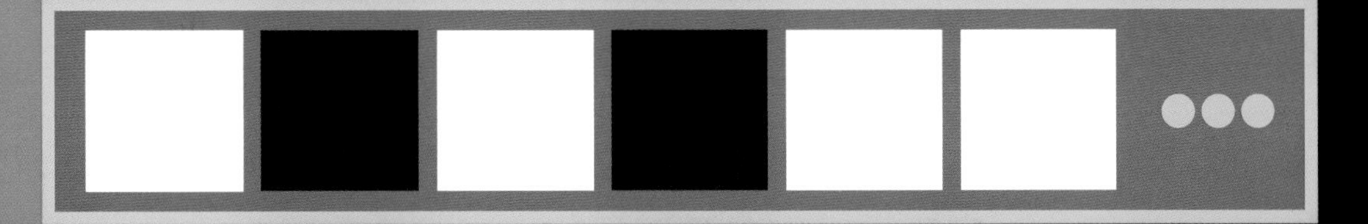

- Bob can't be in row 0 because he doesn't match in column 0.
- Bob can't be in row 1 because he doesn't match in column 1.
- Bob can't be in row 2 because he doesn't match in column 2.

And so on. Therefore ...

BOB IS NOT A ROW ON THE CHART!

$\aleph_0$ and $2^{\aleph_0}$
are not the same size
because that possibility
leads to contradictory
statements.

In other words...

there is more
than one size
of infinity!

It is sort of like you spend your whole life staring at the horizon, wondering what and where it is, and then you find out that there is another horizon beyond the one you had been staring it. In my opinion, this is the sort of thing that should be shouted from the mountaintop.

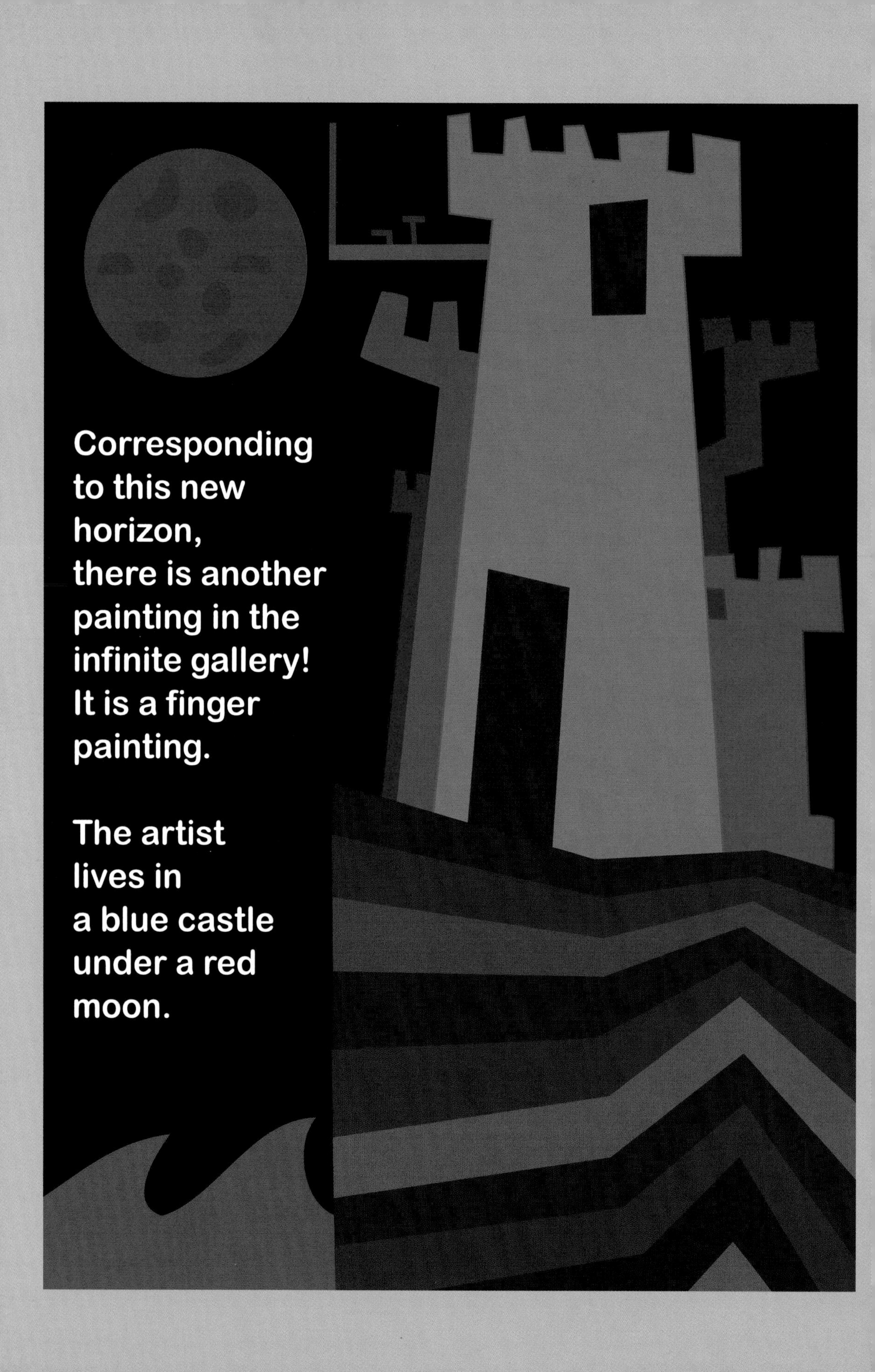
Corresponding
to this new
horizon,
there is another
painting in the
infinite gallery!
It is a finger
painting.

The artist
lives in
a blue castle
under a red
moon.

He sometimes entertains visitors out on his deck. He looks like you from certain directions but not from others. He has hidden features and he gets more intricate the closer you look.

He wears a black or white ring on each finger..

If you are patient, he will show you his fingertips – but not all at once. There is a ritual. He reveals his fingertips slowly.

His two big fingers each branch into smaller fingers, and so on—forever.

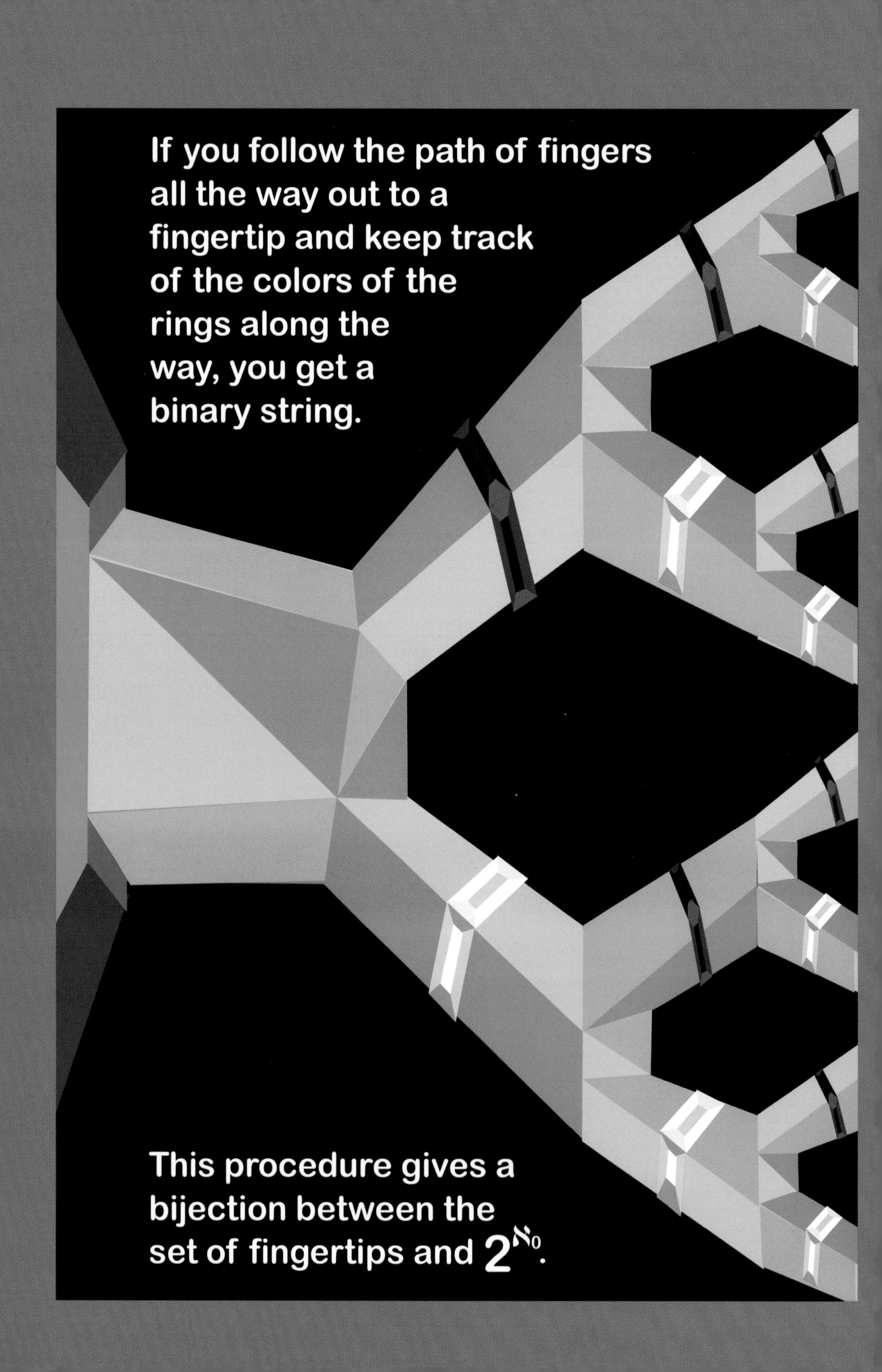
If you follow the path of fingers all the way out to a fingertip and keep track of the colors of the rings along the way, you get a binary string.
This procedure gives a bijection between the set of fingertips and $2^{\aleph_0}$.

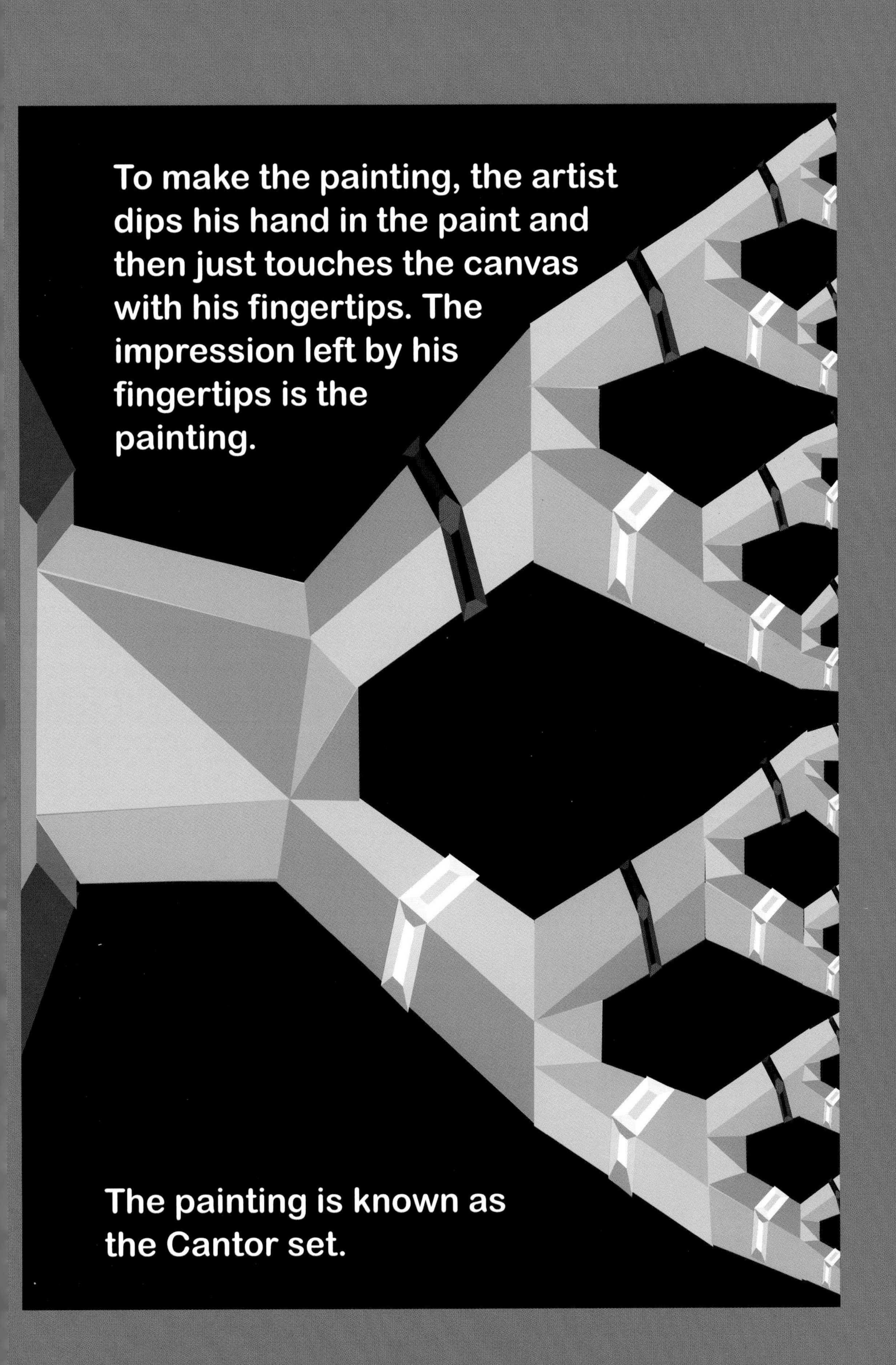
To make the painting, the artist dips his hand in the paint and then just touches the canvas with his fingertips. The impression left by his fingertips is the painting.
The painting is known as the Cantor set.

Here is the traditional view of the Cantor set.

Start with a line segment.

These pink bars are supposed to be line segments, but I thickened them up so that you can see them more easily.

Remove the middle third,

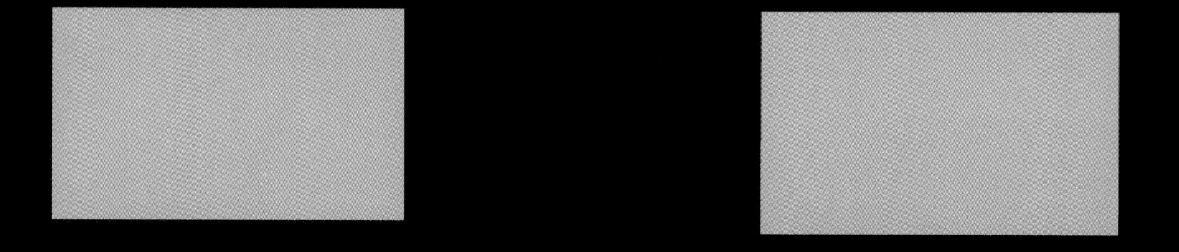

remove the middle third of each half,

and so on.

The Cantor set is the part that remains pink throughout the whole process.

Here is a neat thing. If you connect up the line segments in the right way, you see a caricature of the artist's hand.

I picture it reaching down from the castle to touch the water.

There is
more to
Cantor's
scheme.

He also introduced a way to say when one set is bigger than another.

A **SUBSET** of a set is a new set whose members all belong to the original set.

The subset is called **PROPER** if it doesn't have all the original members.

Here is a set of 3 cards. The next page shows 6 of the 7 proper subsets of this set. The only proper subset not shown is the empty set.

C
A

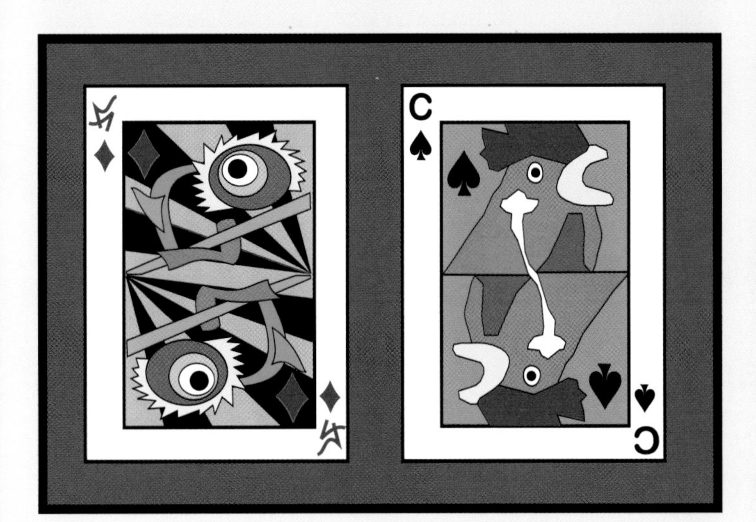
C

A

A

C

If you take away some members of a finite set, you make it smaller.

There is never a bijection between a finite set and one of its proper subsets.

The story is different for infinite sets. The crocodile illustrates a bijection between the set of integers and one of its proper subsets, namely $\aleph_0$.

This chart illustrates a bijection between $\aleph_0$ and a proper subset of $2^{\aleph_0}$.

0 is matched to the binary string that only colors 0 black, and 1 is matched to the binary string that only colors 1 black, and so on.

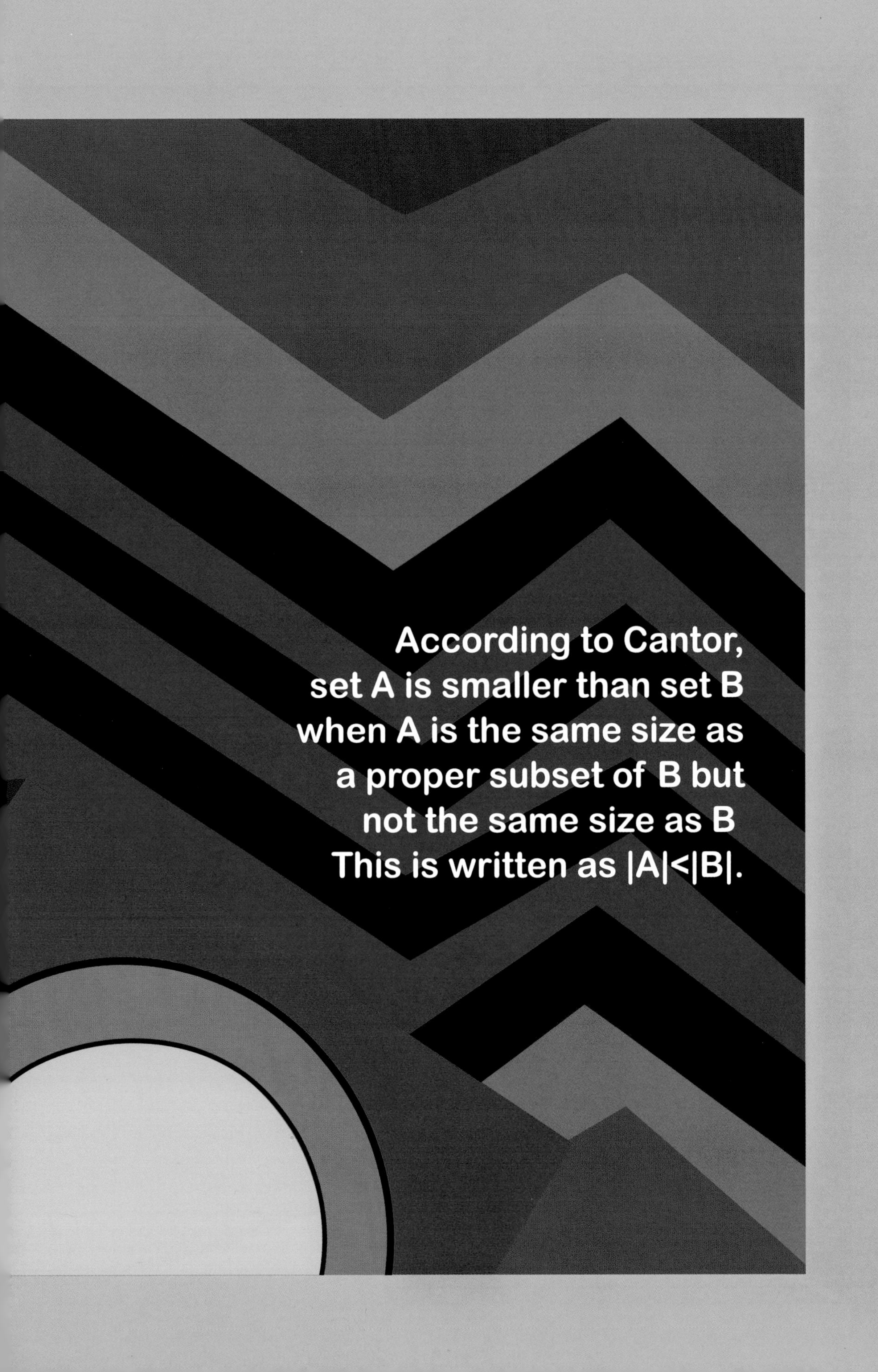
According to Cantor,
set A is smaller than set B
when A is the same size as
a proper subset of B but
not the same size as B
This is written as |A|<|B|.

The Chicken Principle tells us that any infinite set which is the same size as a subset of $\aleph_0$ is also the same size as $\aleph_0$.

We also know that
$\aleph_0 < 2^{\aleph_0}$
This is my vision of a
$2^{\aleph_0}$
chicken.

Cantor's scheme leaves open a fine point that needs to be cleared up.

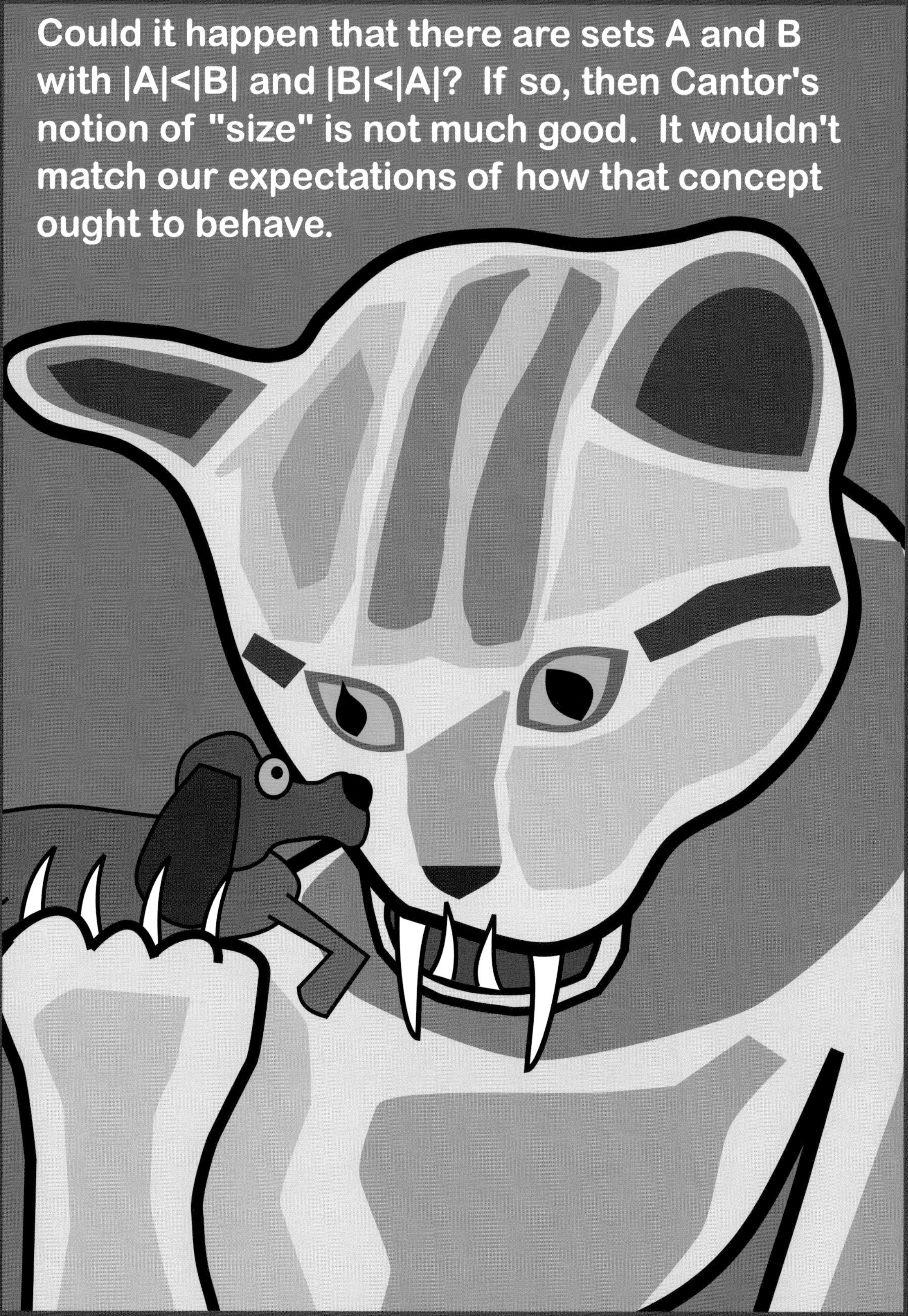

Could it happen that there are sets A and B with $|A|<|B|$ and $|B|<|A|$? If so, then Cantor's notion of "size" is not much good. It wouldn't match our expectations of how that concept ought to behave.

Luckily,
the
Cantor-
Bernstein
Theorem
rules out
this funny
behavior.

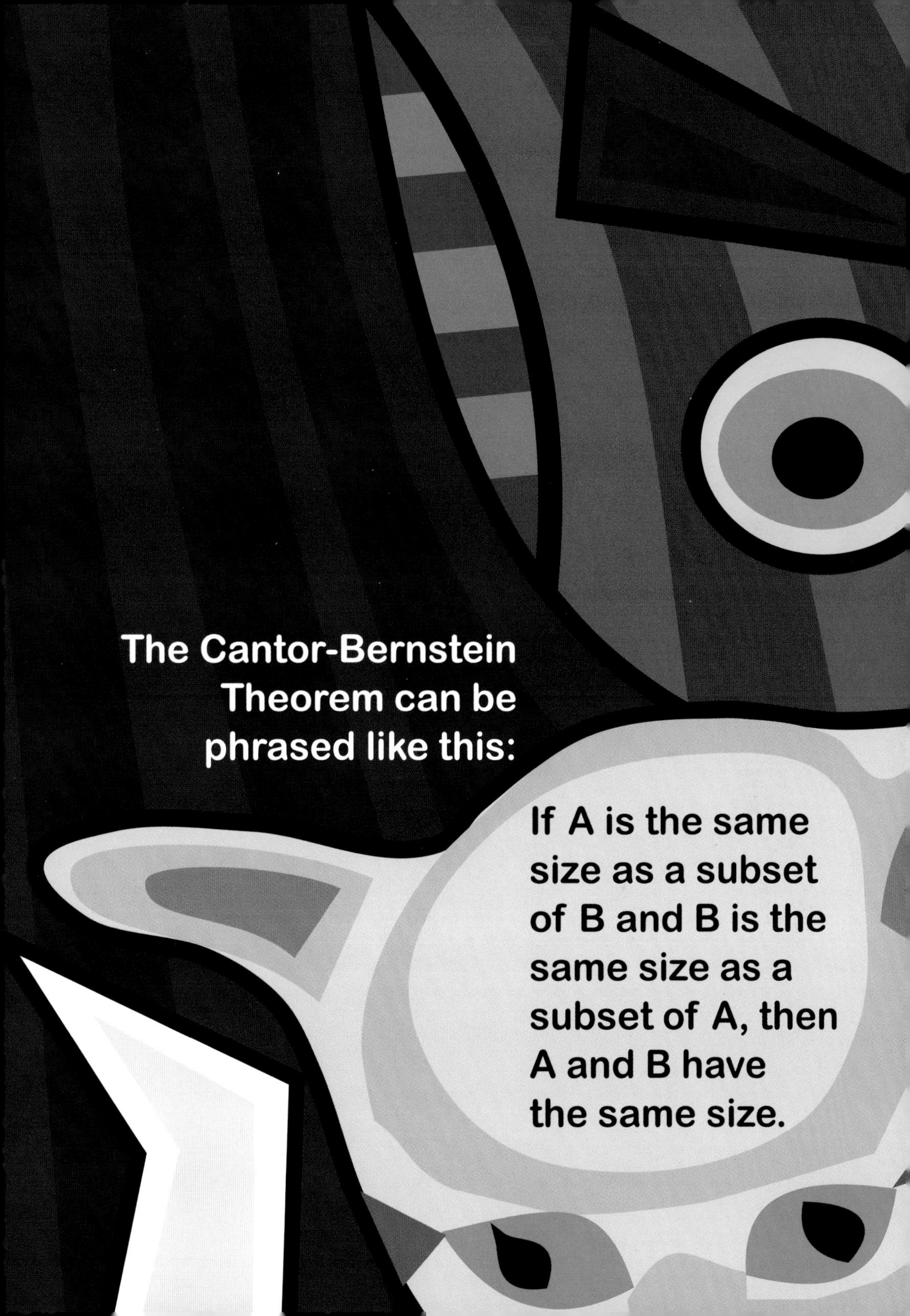
The Cantor-Bernstein
Theorem can be
phrased like this:
If A is the same
size as a subset
of B and B is the
same size as a
subset of A, then
A and B have
the same size.

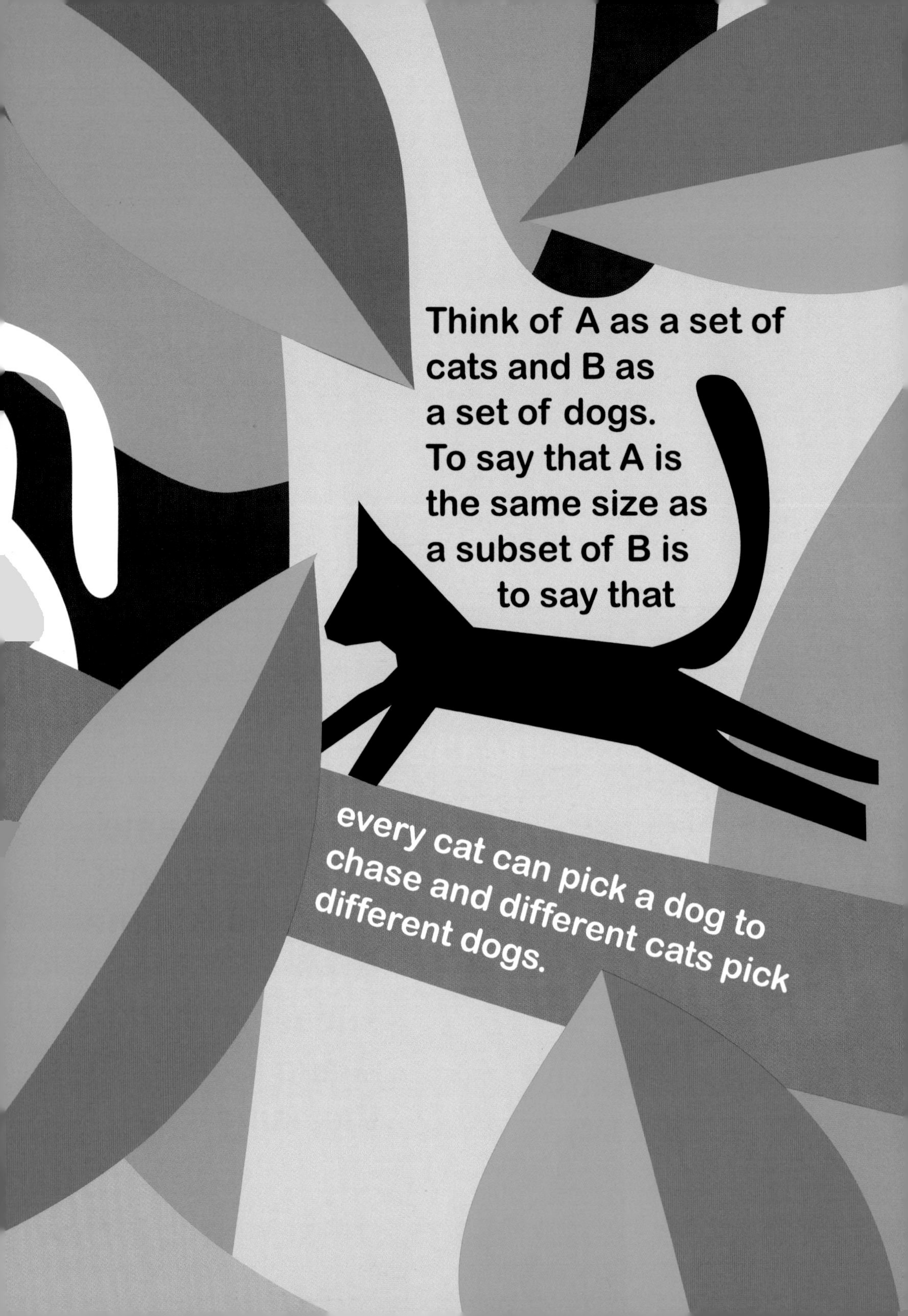
Think of A as a set of
cats and B as
a set of dogs.
To say that A is
the same size as
a subset of B is
to say that
every cat can pick a dog to
chase and different cats pick
different dogs.

Likewise, every dog can pick a cat to chase and different dogs pick different cats.

Your pets are chasing each other around the yard. You keep track of who is chasing whom, and you notice 4 kinds of patterns.

1. Chasing loops which involve an even number of animals. Match each cat to the dog it chases within the loop.

2. Chasing chains which have no start or end, like the integers. Match each cat to the dog it chases within the chain.

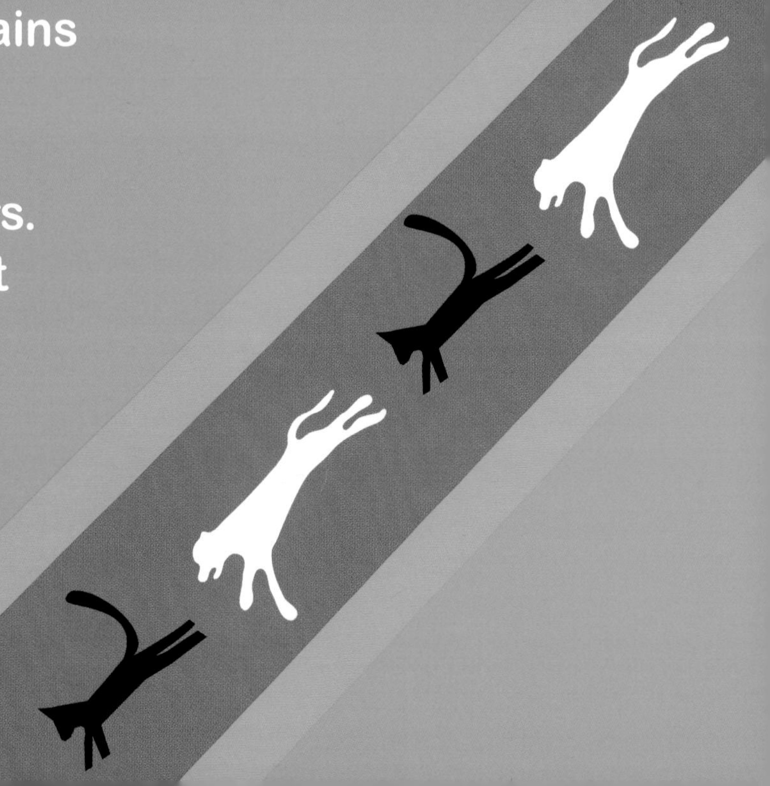

3.
Chasing chains which start with a cat and have no end, like the counting numbers. Match each cat to the dog it chases.
4.
Chasing chains which start with a dog and have no end. Match each cat to the dog chasing it. That's it. We're done! Cats and dogs are all matched.

That takes care of the fine point. As a bonus, the Cantor-Bernstein Theorem is useful when it comes to figuring out things about the sizes of infinite sets—like the set of real numbers. (A real number is essentially just an infinite decimal expansion.)

Here is one way to match each real number with a binary string:

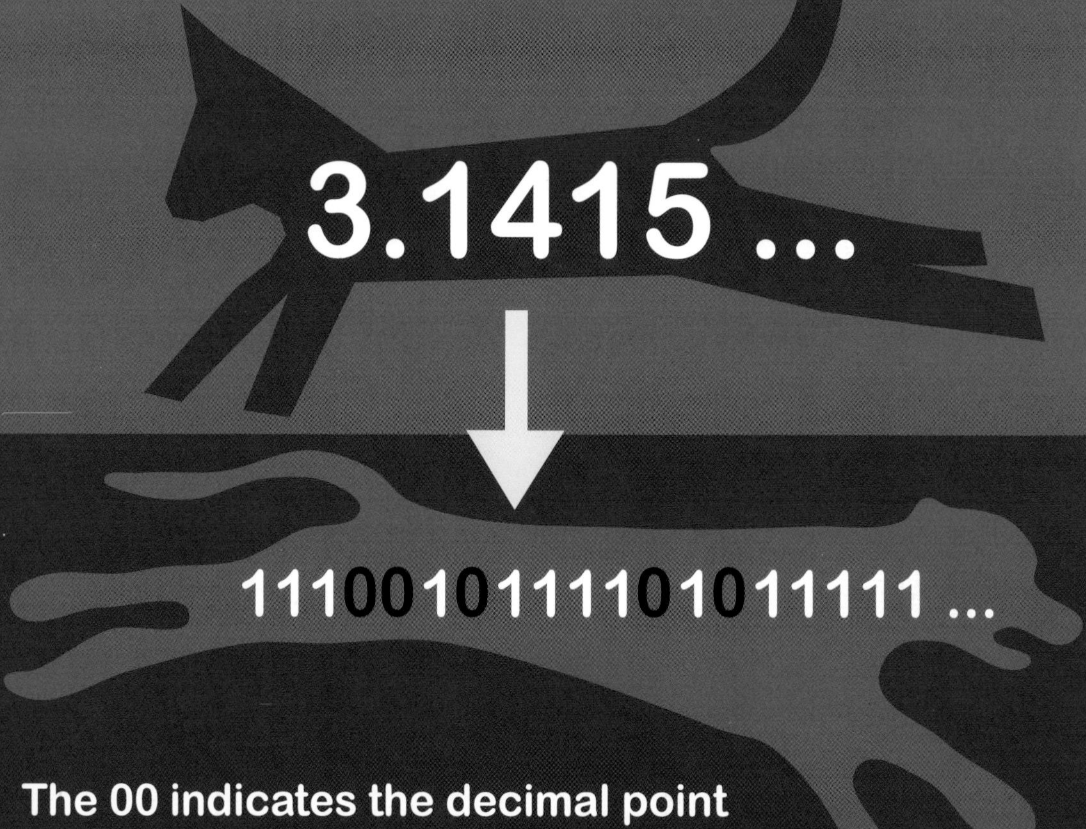

3.1415 ...

11100101111010111111 ...

The 00 indicates the decimal point and each 0 separates a string of 1's corresponding to a digit.
Different cats chase different dogs.

At the same time, you can match each binary string to a real number, like this:

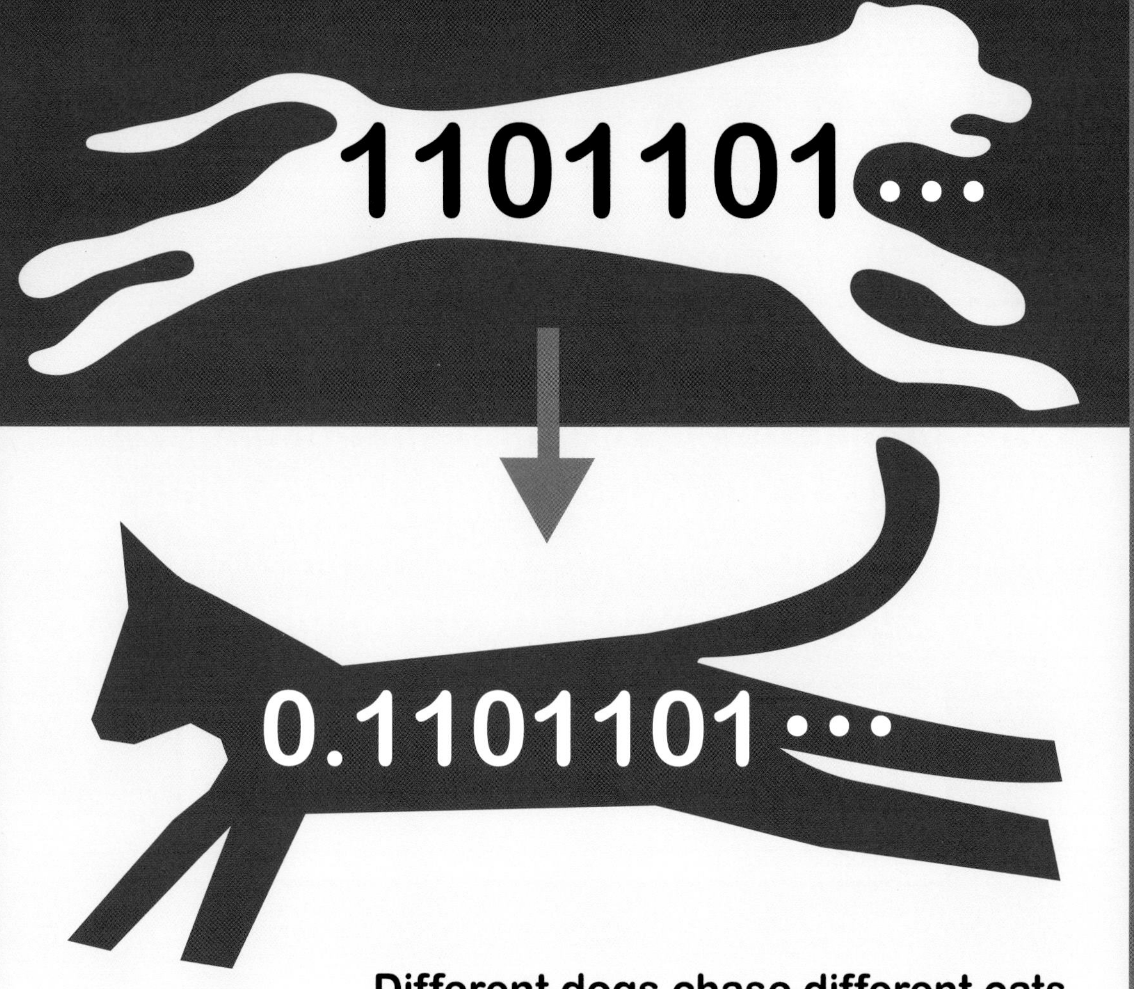

Different dogs chase different cats.

The first matching procedure tells us that the set of real numbers is the same size as a subset of $2^{\aleph_0}$.

The second matching procedure says the reverse. So, the Cantor-Bernstein Theorem says that the two sets have the same size.

The set of real numbers is really the same thing as the set of points on the line. So, the set of points on the line has the same size as $2^{\aleph_0}$.

What about the set of points in the plane? Well, first of all, you can match each binary string to a different point on the line, and then you can draw the line in the plane:

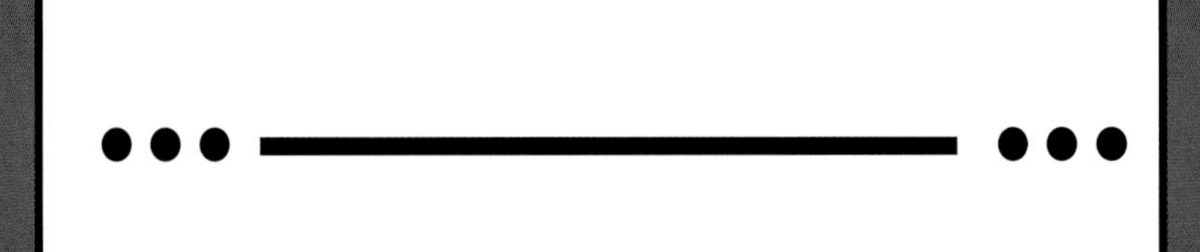

So $2^{\aleph_0}$ is the same size as a subset of the plane.

At the same time, each point in the plane can be described by a pair of binary strings.

11100101111010111110...

3 . 1 4 1 5...

2 . 7 1...

11001111111010...

Just take the coordinates of the point and convert them to binary strings.

Now shuffle the binary strings together:

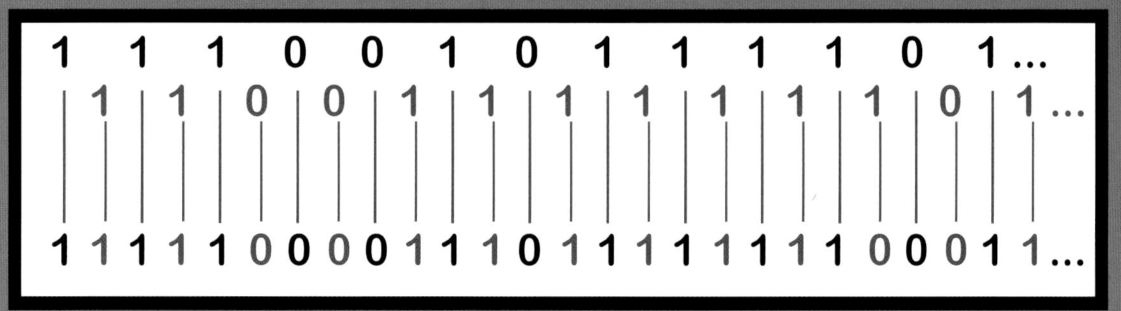

This procedure matches each point in the plane with its own binary sequence.

So, the Cantor-Bernstein Theorem says that the set of points in the plane has the same size as $2^{\aleph_0}$.

The same argument works in 3D as well.

$2^{\aleph_0}$ is the size of (idealized) space!

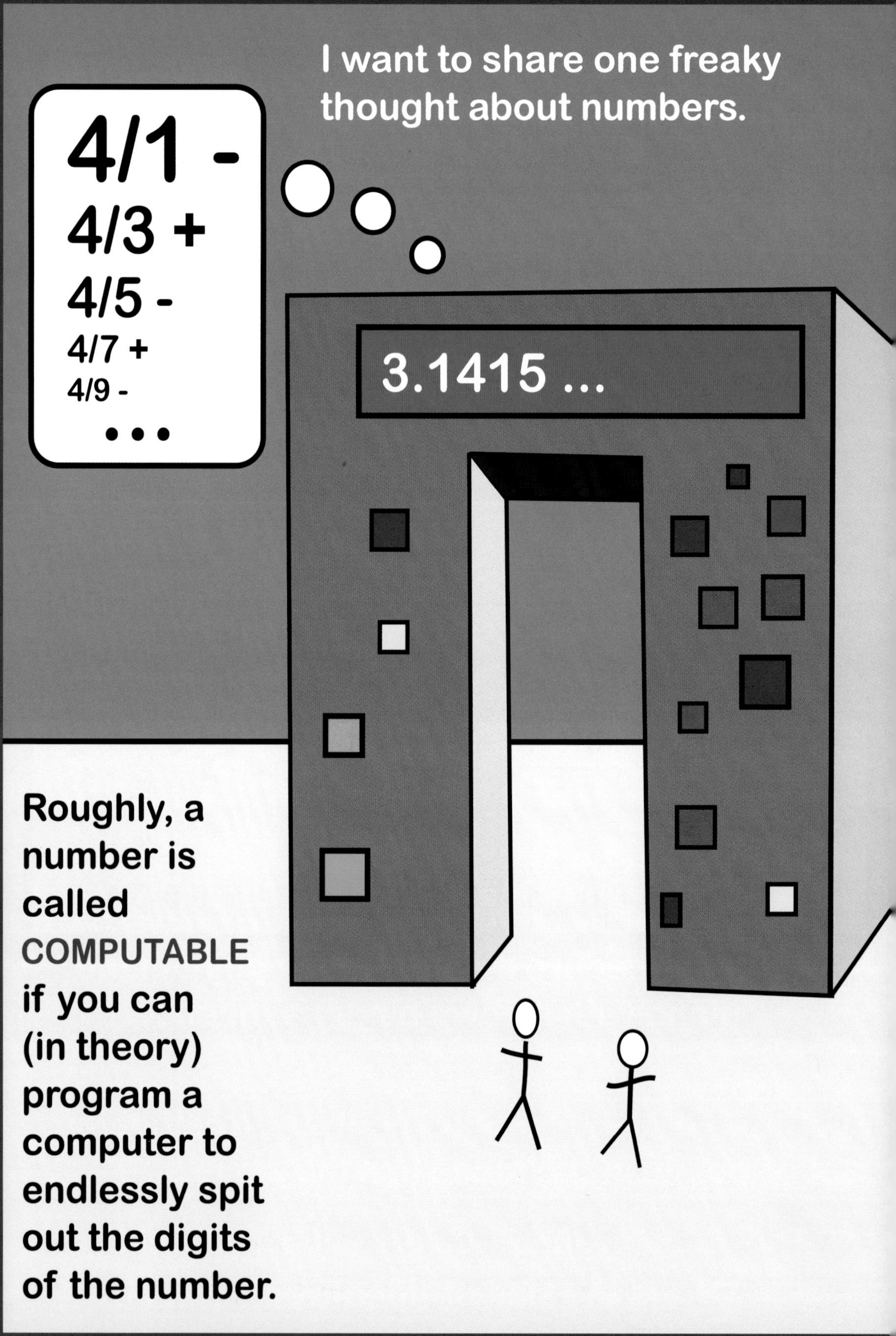

I want to share one freaky thought about numbers.

4/1 -
4/3 +
4/5 -
4/7 +
4/9 -
• • •

3.1415 ...

Roughly, a number is called COMPUTABLE if you can (in theory) program a computer to endlessly spit out the digits of the number.

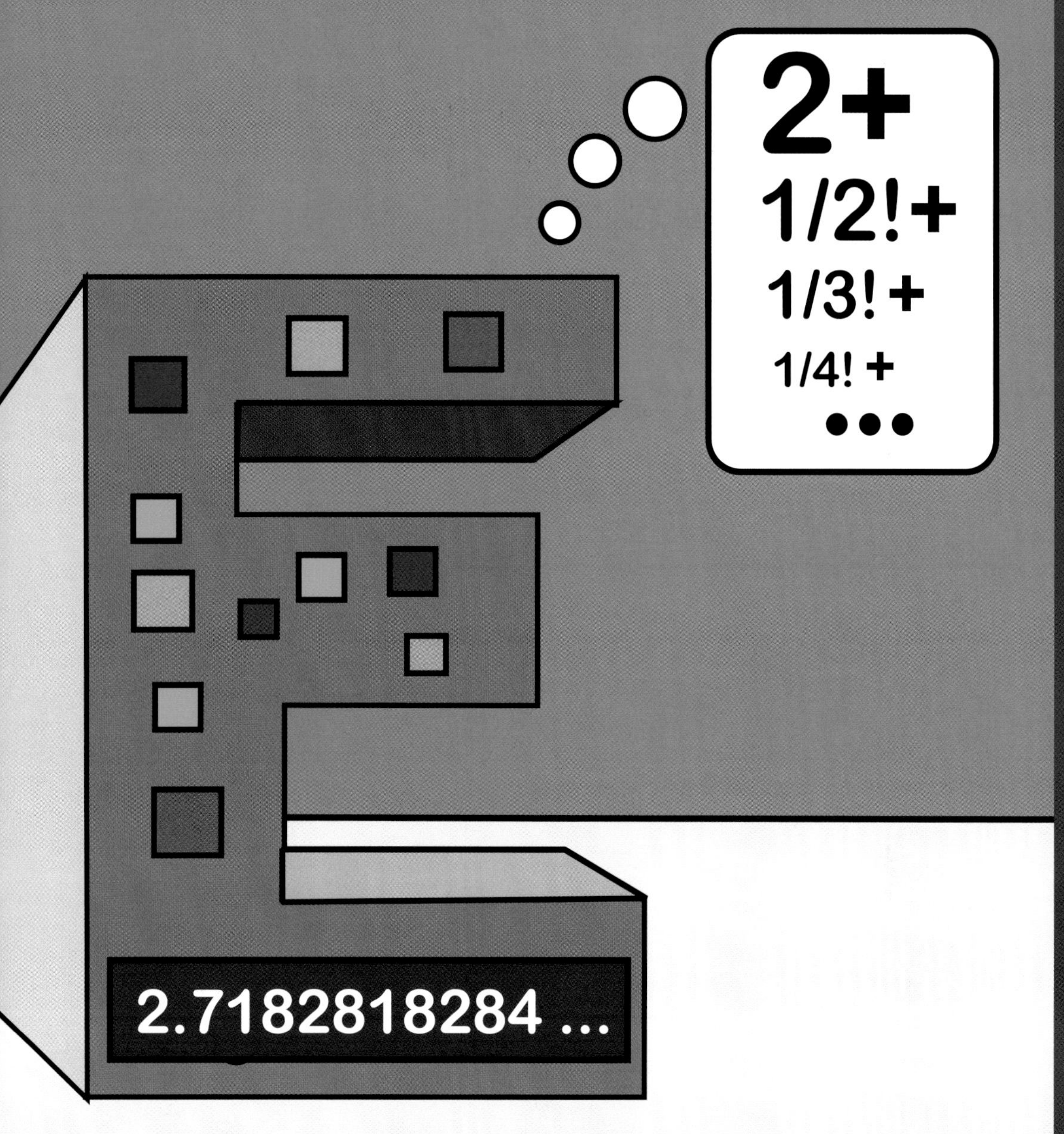

Every familiar kind of number is computable: rational numbers, roots of polynomials with integer coefficients, limits of series you might happen to know. You name it! All computable. But ...

the set of all possible computer programs you could run on a finite computer, like the set of finite text messages, is the same size as $\aleph_0$.

This is smaller than the set of all possible real numbers, which has size $2^{\aleph_0}$.

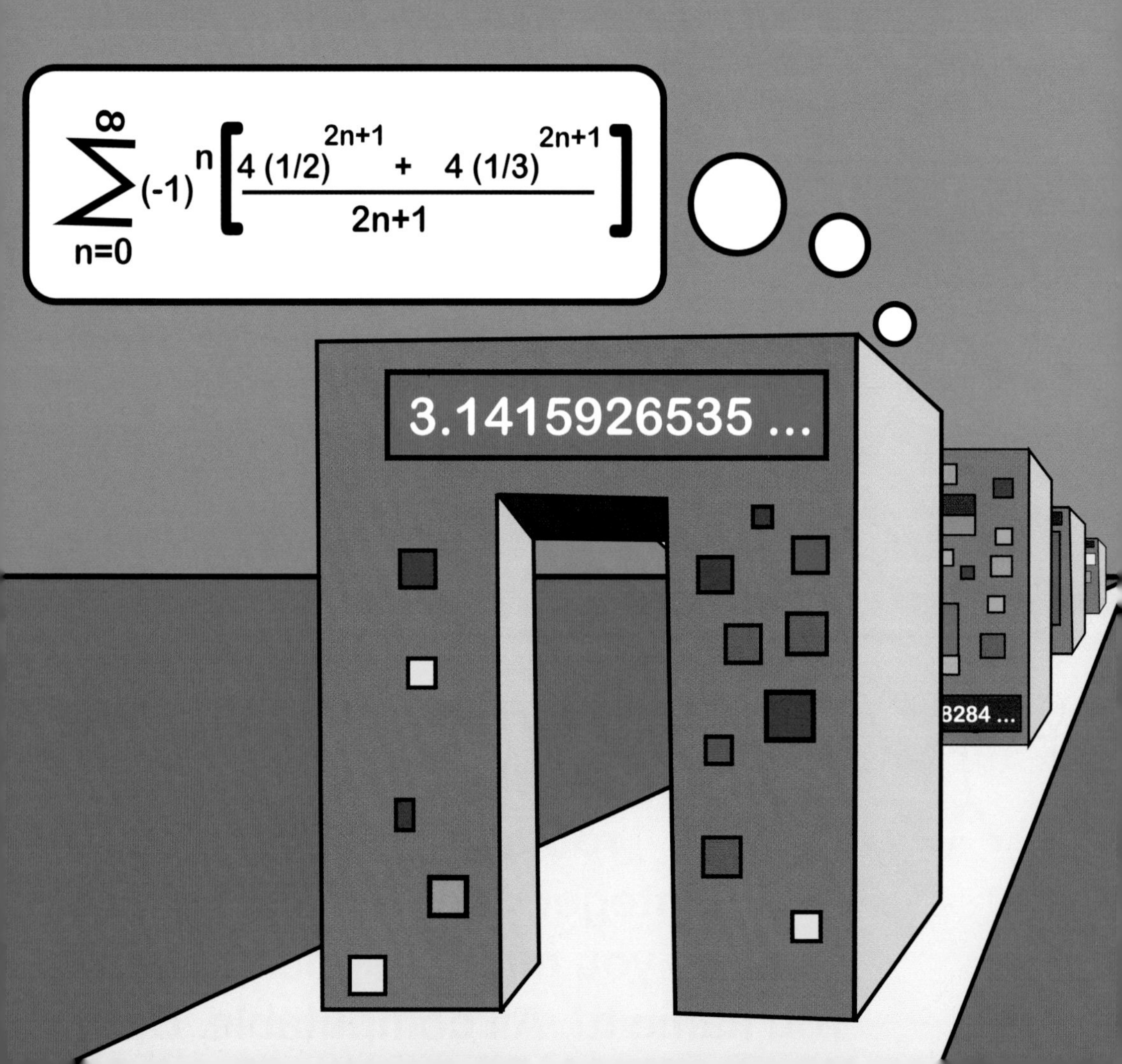

So, there are vastly more noncomputable real numbers than there are computable ones. The same goes for points in the plane or in space. If you pick a point at random, its location will not be computable, which is to say essentially that it will be nameless and unknowable.

Sometimes when I stare at a telephone wire or a tabletop I remember that it is saturated with impenetrable mystery.

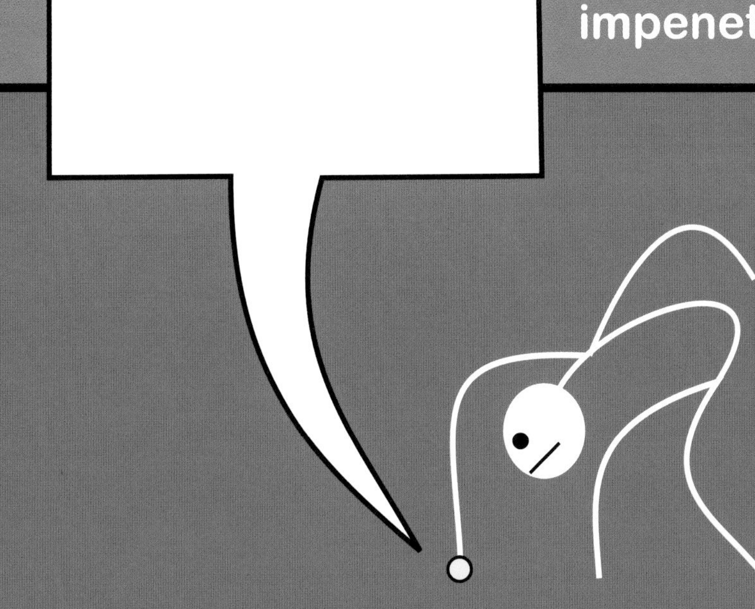

I want to say more about the curator of the infinite gallery. She also grows more intricate the closer you look.
Have a nice day!

Take, for example, one of her eyes.

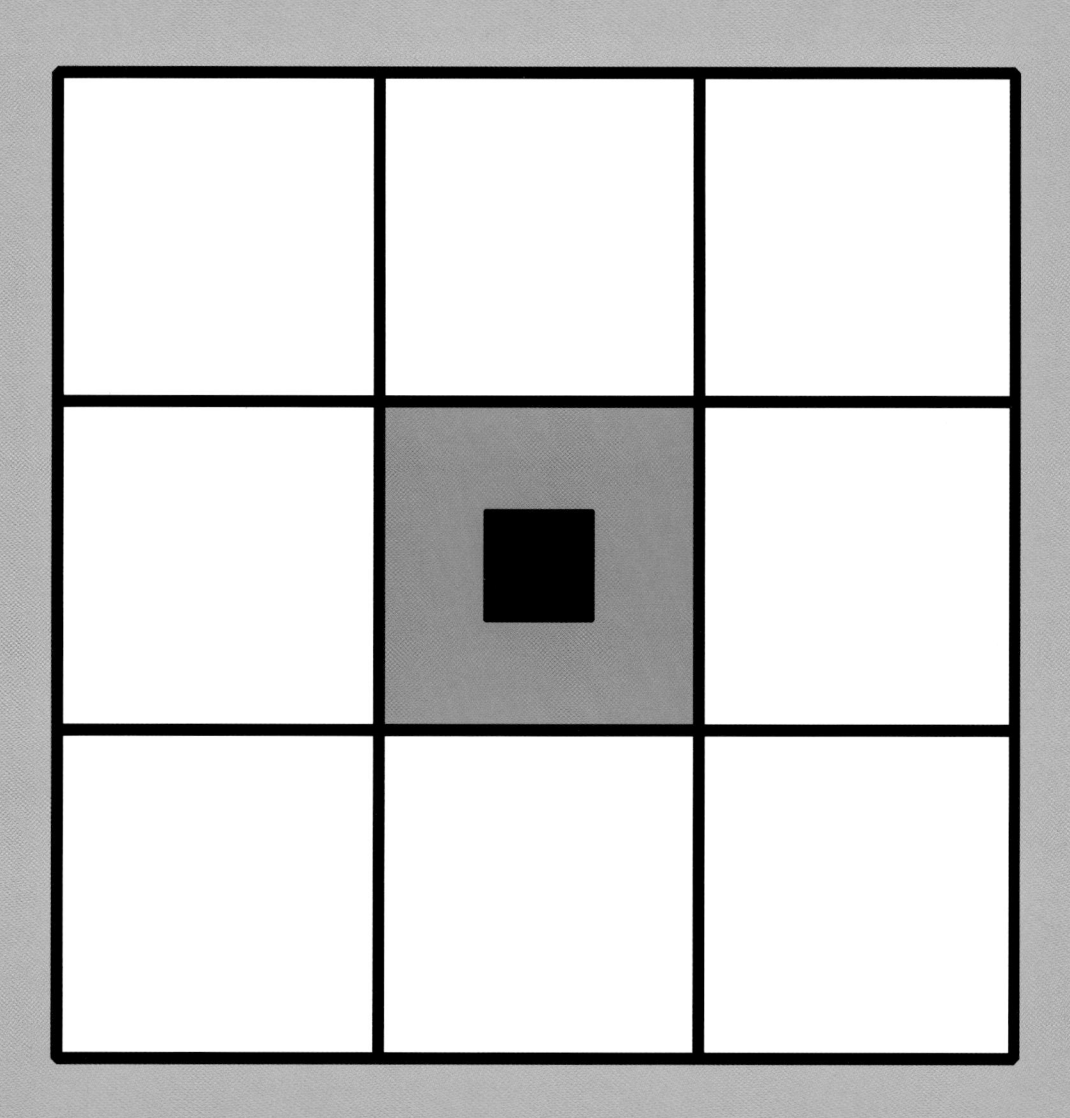

At first glance, it looks like this.

But when you look more closely,

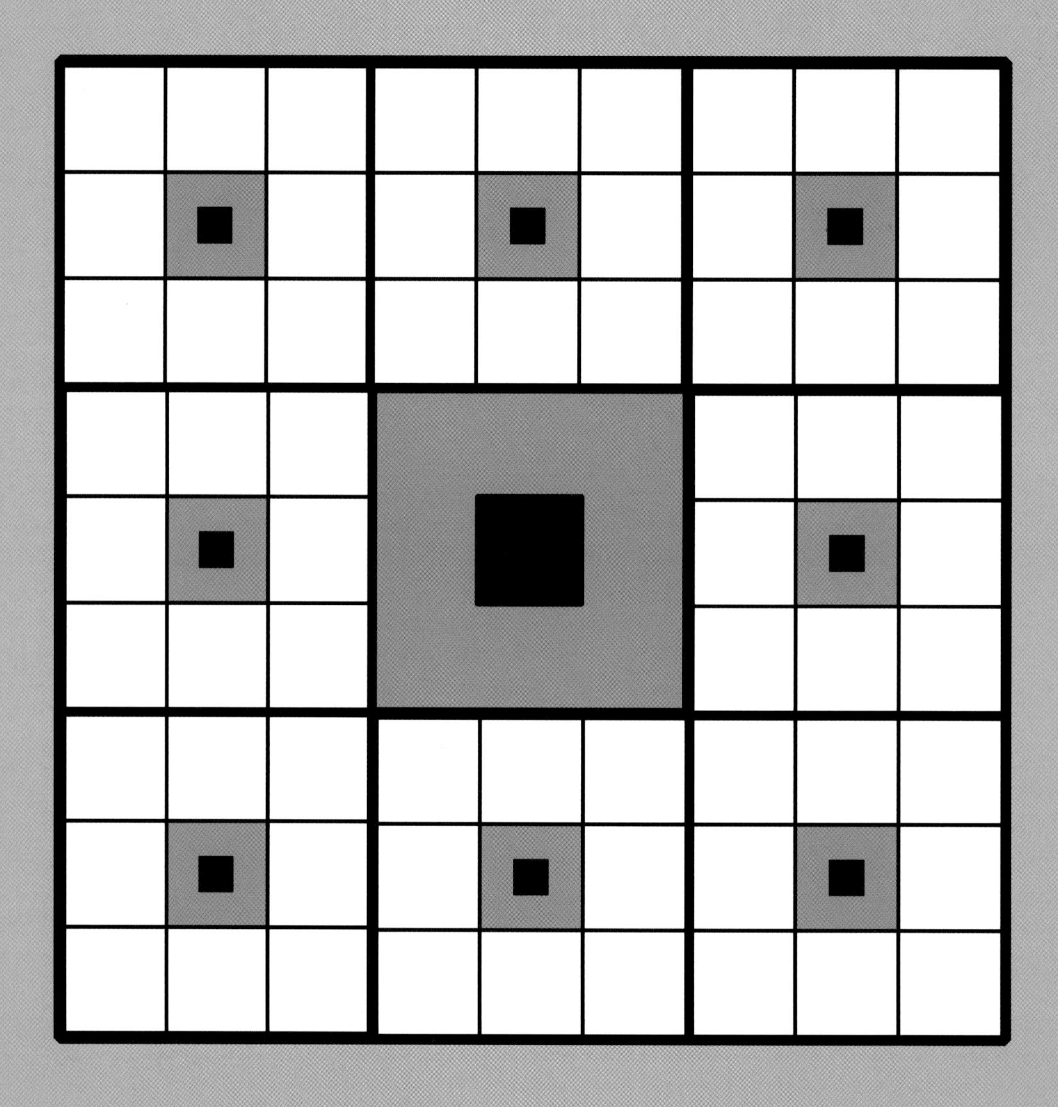

you notice that the original pattern appears in each of the white squares.

When you look more closely still, you again see the original pattern in each white square, and so on.

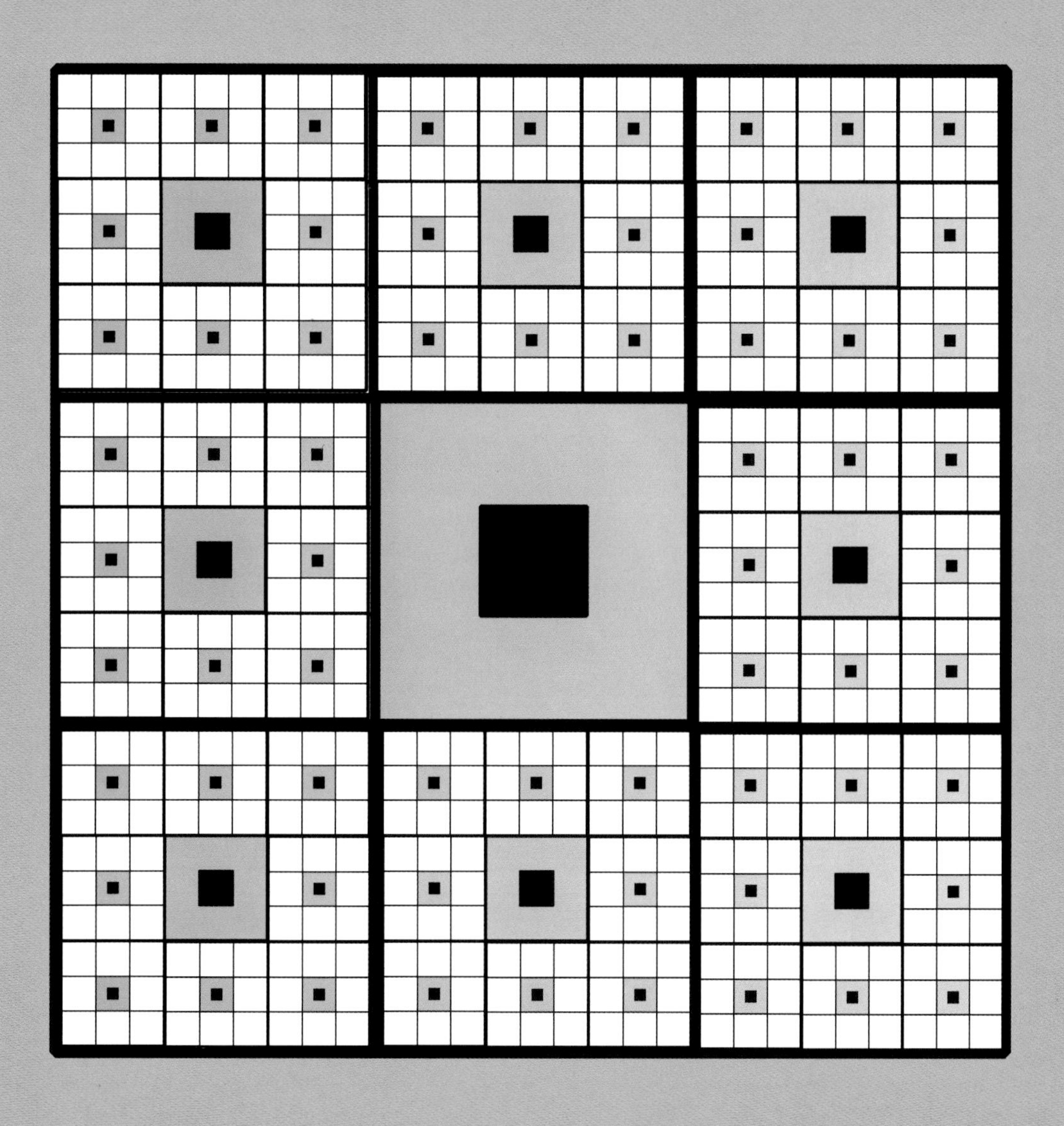

If you look closely you can see the Cantor set in her eye.

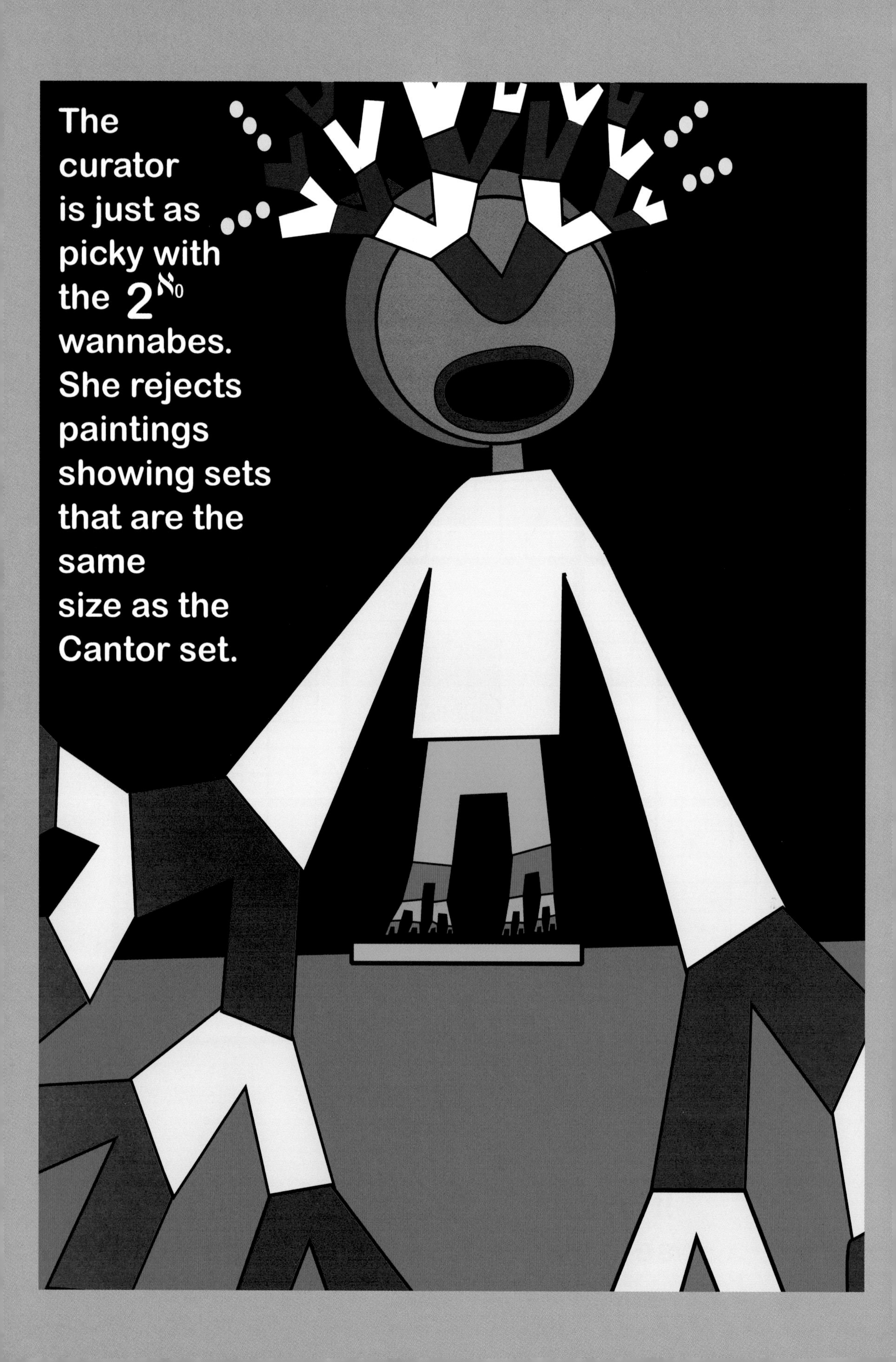
The curator is just as picky with the $2^{\aleph_0}$ wannabes. She rejects paintings showing sets that are the same size as the Cantor set.

So you might again ask what else is in the gallery. What about bigger infinite sets?

Let's revisit Cantor's diagonal argument

The set of all subsets of a set A is called the POWER SET of A. It is written like this → 2^A

You might worry that $2^{\aleph_0}$ has 2 meanings:

1. the set of binary strings,
2. the power set of $\aleph_0$.

Don't worry. These two sets are the same set in disguise. You can match a subset of $\aleph_0$ with the binary string that colors the elements of that subset black. For instance.

$\{1,3,5,...\}$ ↔ ■□■□■□ ...

Could A and 2^A have the same size?

Think of A as a collection of animals.

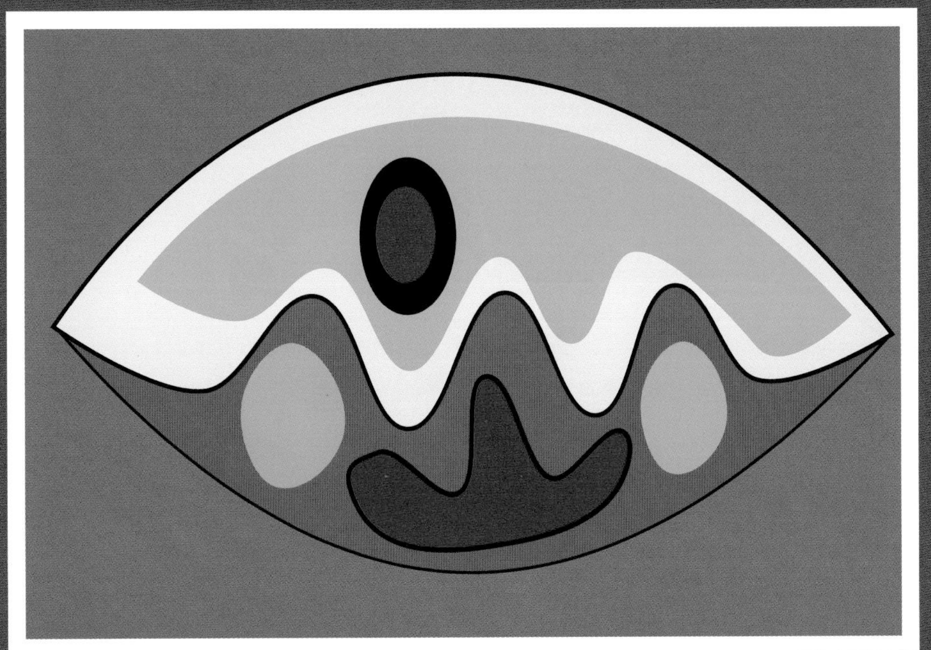

Here are two of the members of A.

Think of a subset of A as a group photo involving some of the animals. A bijection between A and its power set would mean that there was a way to match up the animals and their group photos.

Say that an animal is happy precisely when it sees itself in the group photo it gets. The cat is happy but this guy is not.

One of the photos shows the set of all the unhappy animals. Here is part of the photo.

One of the animals must be matched
with this unhappy photo. Let's say it
is this one.

Suppose this guy is happy.

This situation is not possible.

Suppose he is unhappy.

This situation is also impossible.

So, no animal gets the unhappy photo. The assumption that A and 2^A are the same size leads to a contradiction. That means that they can't be the same size.

On the other hand, A is the same size as the set of PORTRAITS in the power set—group photos just showing one animal. This is easy: Just match each animal to its portrait.

According to the definition $|A|<|2^A|$.

And this result tells us that ...

there are infinitely many sizes of infinity!

$\aleph_0$ $2^{\aleph_0}$ $2^{2^{\aleph_0}}$...

And
there
is
no
largest
size!

You could picture $2^{2^{\aleph_0}}$ as the set of all black and white playing cards.

But this is just a manner of speaking. To picture this set...

... you would
have to picture every
variant of every image
you know, every tiny
change, all possible
patterns.

No way!
You can't
PICTURE $2^{2^{\aleph_0}}$ or any of the larger sets in the hierarchy.

$2^{2^{\aleph_0}}$

If you tried to look
into one of the
other rooms, maybe
you'd get some weird
alien hand in your
face and you'd
experience
a blinding flash
of light. That is all.
We can't afford
the membership
dues needed to
see the other rooms.

And, if you must know, the infinite hierarchy you get by taking power set after power set is just the FIRST hierarchy of infinities. There is a hierarchy of hierarchies, and so on.

In this context, the words "and so on" do not do justice to the full extent of what is going on. The infinite gallery has room after room, horizon after horizon!

Or maybe the gallery
doesn't exist.

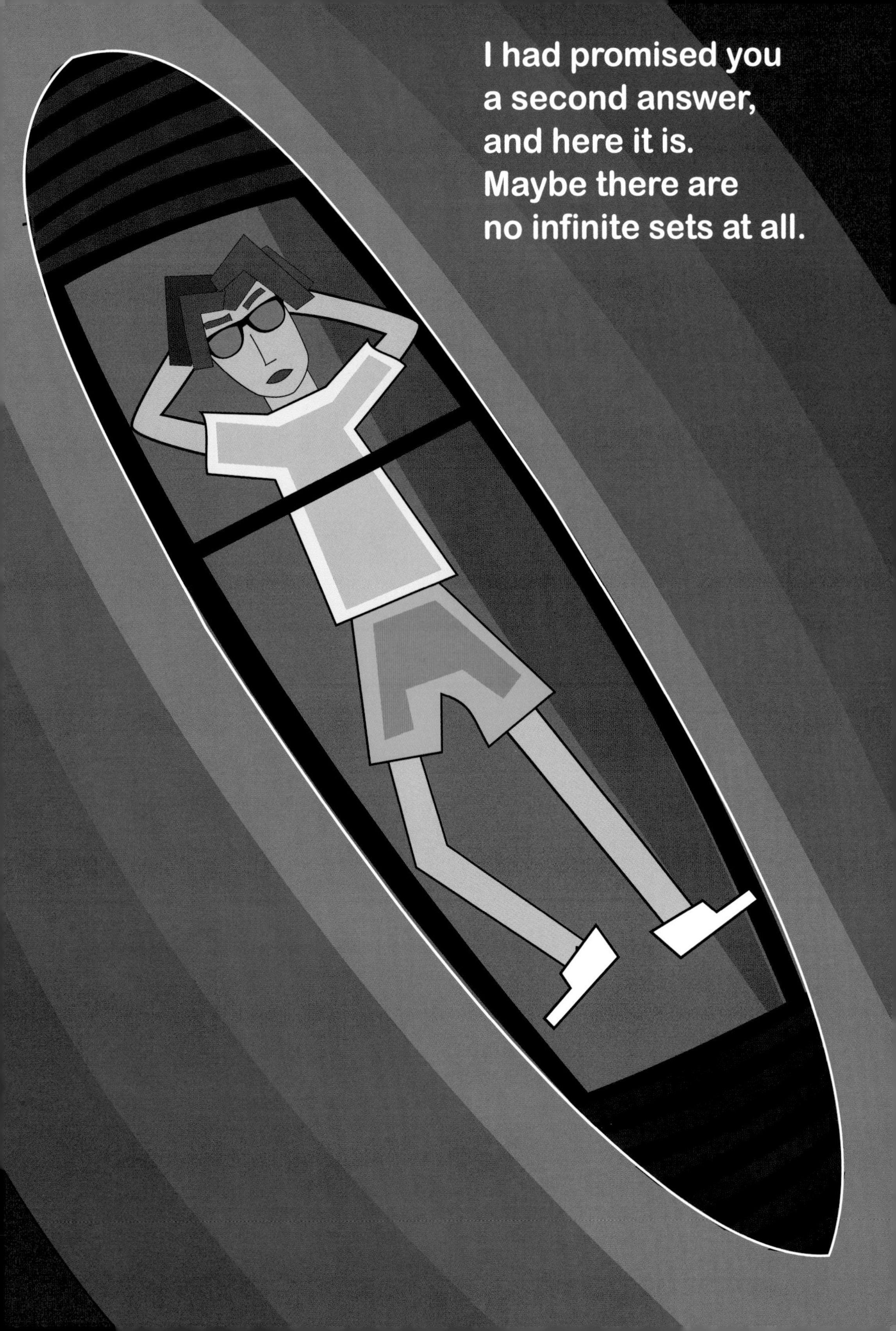
I had promised you a second answer, and here it is. Maybe there are no infinite sets at all.

See, mathematics is founded on axioms.

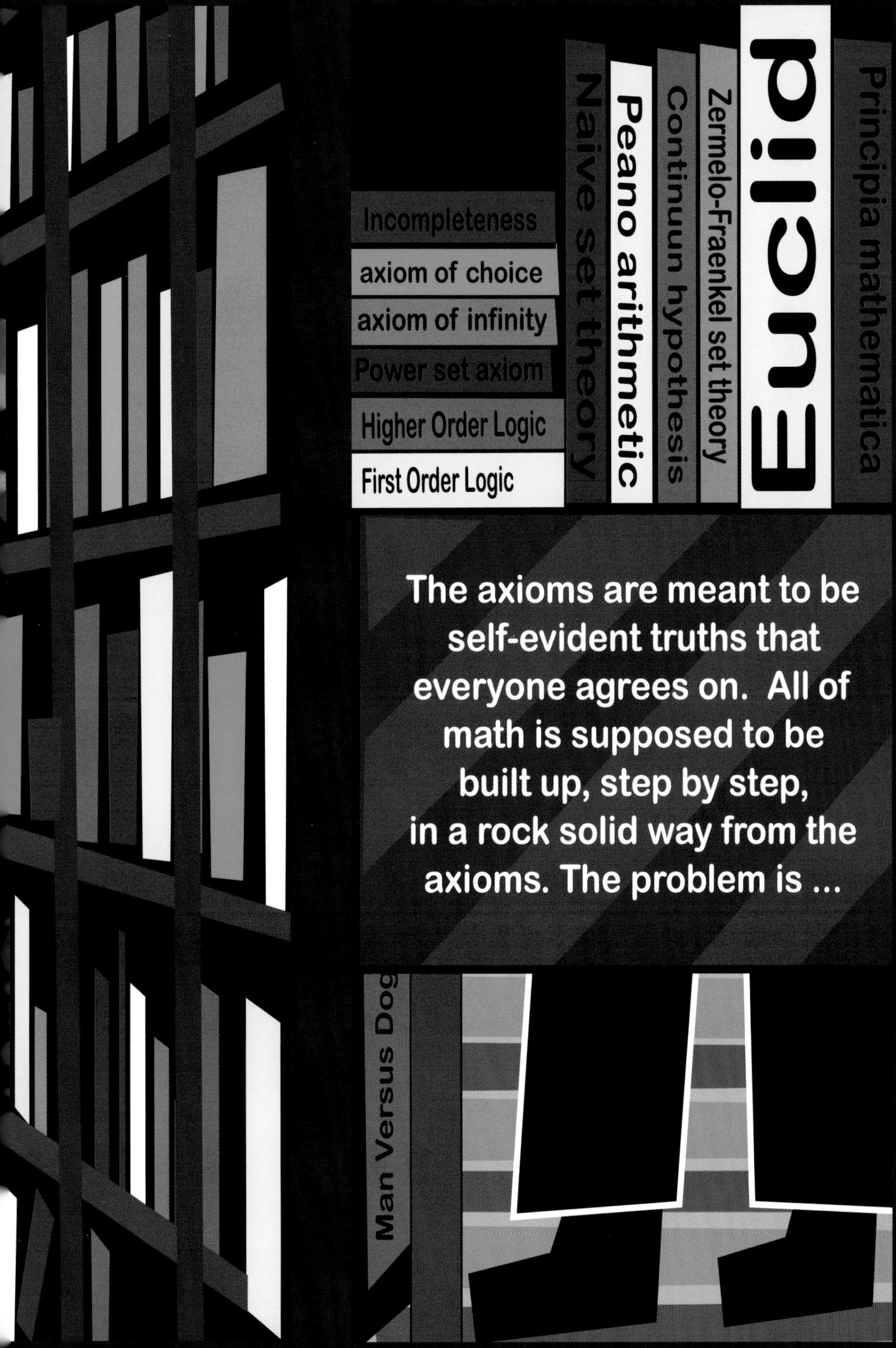

Incompleteness
axiom of choice
axiom of infinity
Power set axiom
Higher Order Logic
First Order Logic
Naive set theory
Peano arithmetic
Continuun hypothesis
Zermelo-Fraenkel set theory
Euclid
Principia mathematica

The axioms are meant to be self-evident truths that everyone agrees on. All of math is supposed to be built up, step by step, in a rock solid way from the axioms. The problem is ...

Man Versus Dog

the axioms evolve, like scientific theories, and not everyone agrees on them.

In the past, people have put forward axioms which seemed obvious, but then later on it turned out that they led to inconsistencies in the system.

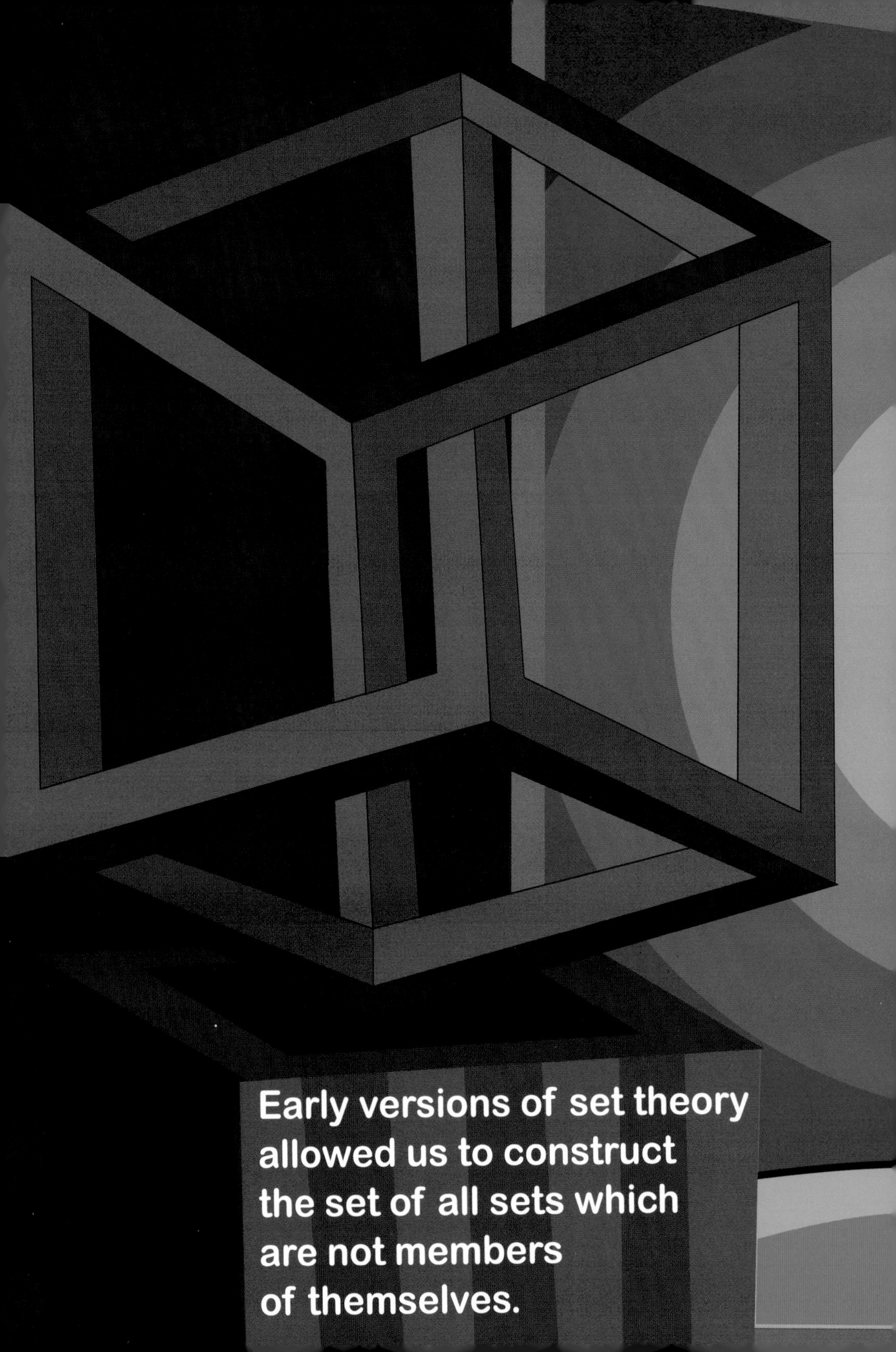
Early versions of set theory
allowed us to construct
the set of all sets which
are not members
of themselves.

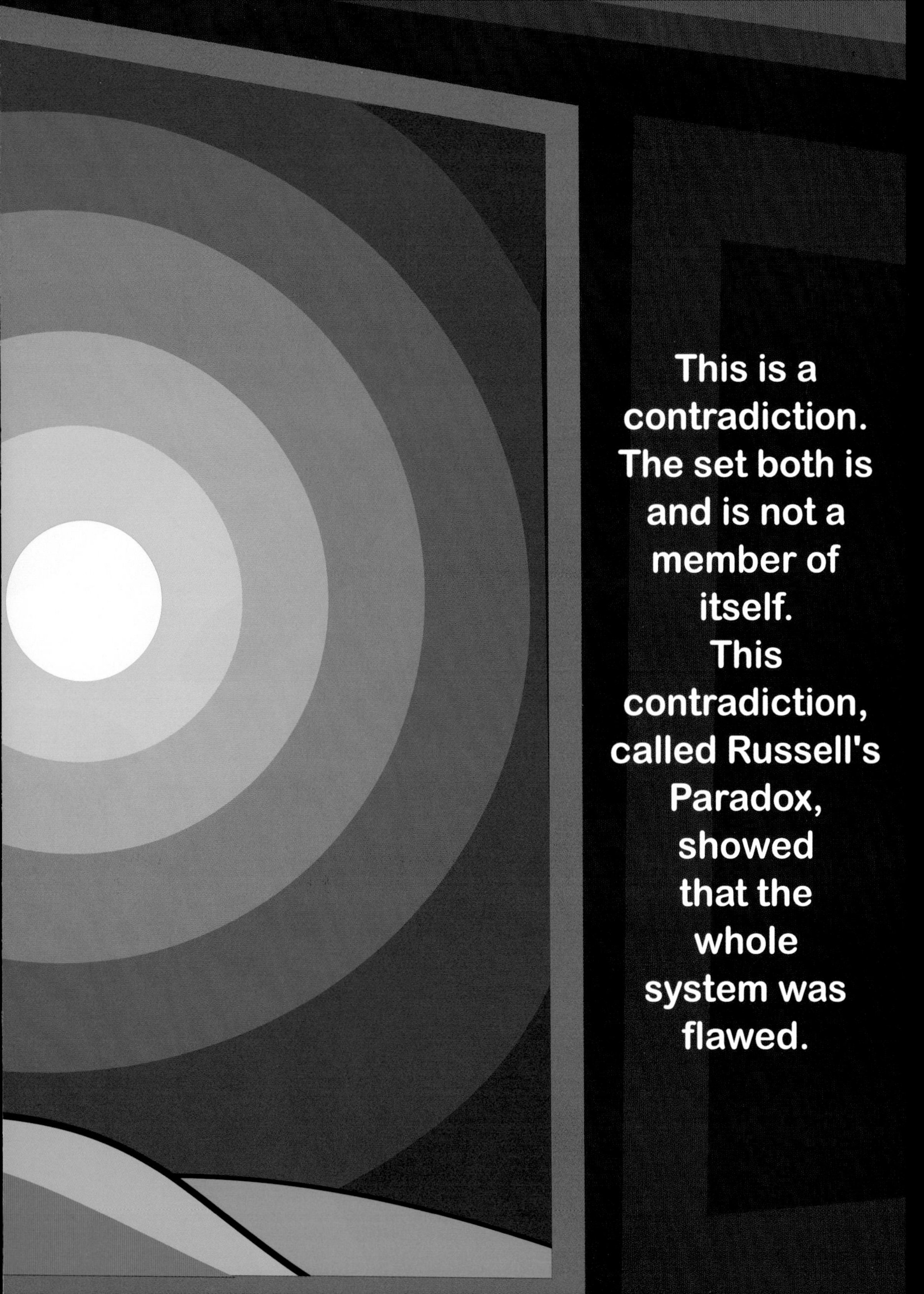
This is a
contradiction.
The set both is
and is not a
member of
itself.
This
contradiction,
called Russell's
Paradox,
showed
that the
whole
system was
flawed.

The old axioms had to be refined a bit in order to avoid Russell's Paradox while still allowing the same general kind of reasoning. After all, Russell's Paradox is just a shade away from Cantor's diagonal argument.

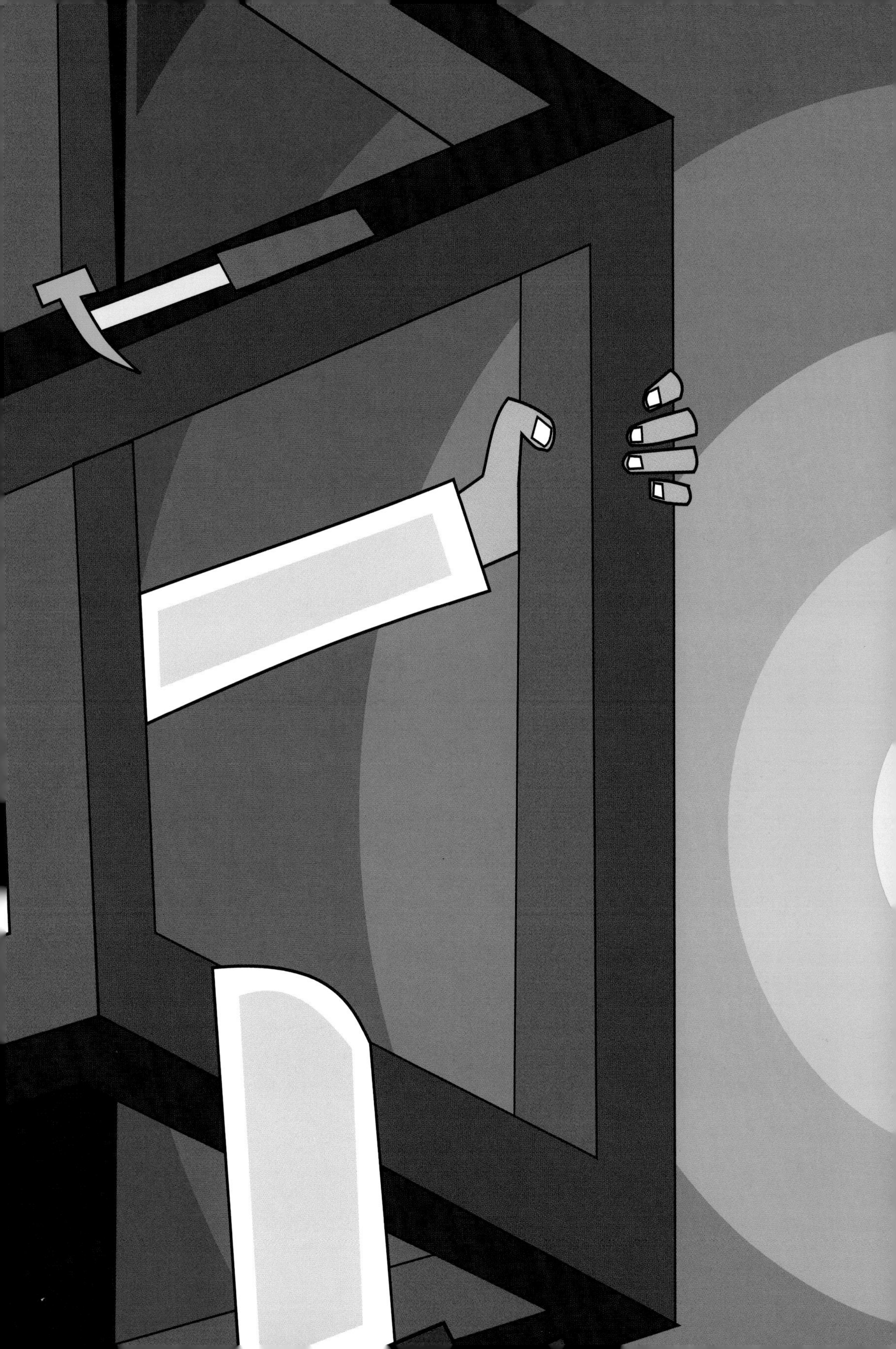

You could think of mathematics as a beautiful mansion, but some of the back rooms need repairs from time to time. The infinite gallery is a wing of the mansion, but maybe they are not selling tickets on the day you visit.

Maybe there are hidden problems with some of the axioms which provide for the existence of infinite sets.

NO
SOLICITORS
When I think about
this possibility, I
imagine that the
number line is
a long and
dusty road that
ends in a shack...
and there is some wild-eyed
dude out in front who tells visitors
that they can't go on because the
numbers have run out.

One of my friends suggests that maybe it is more like the number line gets overrun with weeds and somehow you lose your way as you walk along.

Or maybe the set of counting numbers exists but there is some problem with the power set axiom and really it is not possible to form the set of all binary strings. Maybe if you try to follow all those branching paths out to their ends

some of them
trail off into
nothing or
get hopelessly
entangled.

I'm not sure if I take these analogies seriously, but I can imagine that we might have to give up some of our axioms in light of new ideas and insights as we extend our intellectual range.

than I am in shapes and patterns.
It seems to me that the vivid
mathematical patterns I like ...

have a life
of their
own ...

... and
would
find their
expression
regardless
of the
axioms.

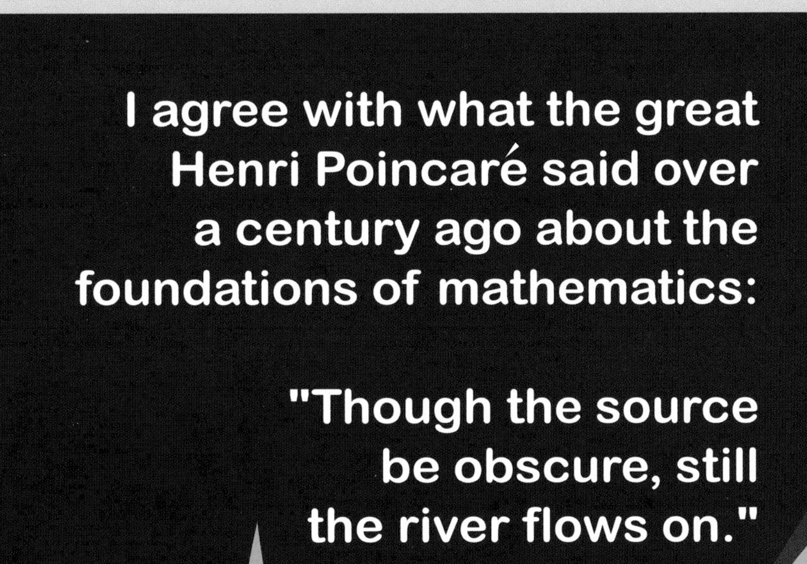
I agree with what the great
Henri Poincaré said over
a century ago about the
foundations of mathematics:
"Though the source
be obscure, still
the river flows on."

So, ARE THERE
infinitely many
sizes of infinity?
Well, formally
speaking, all I
can tell you
is that ...

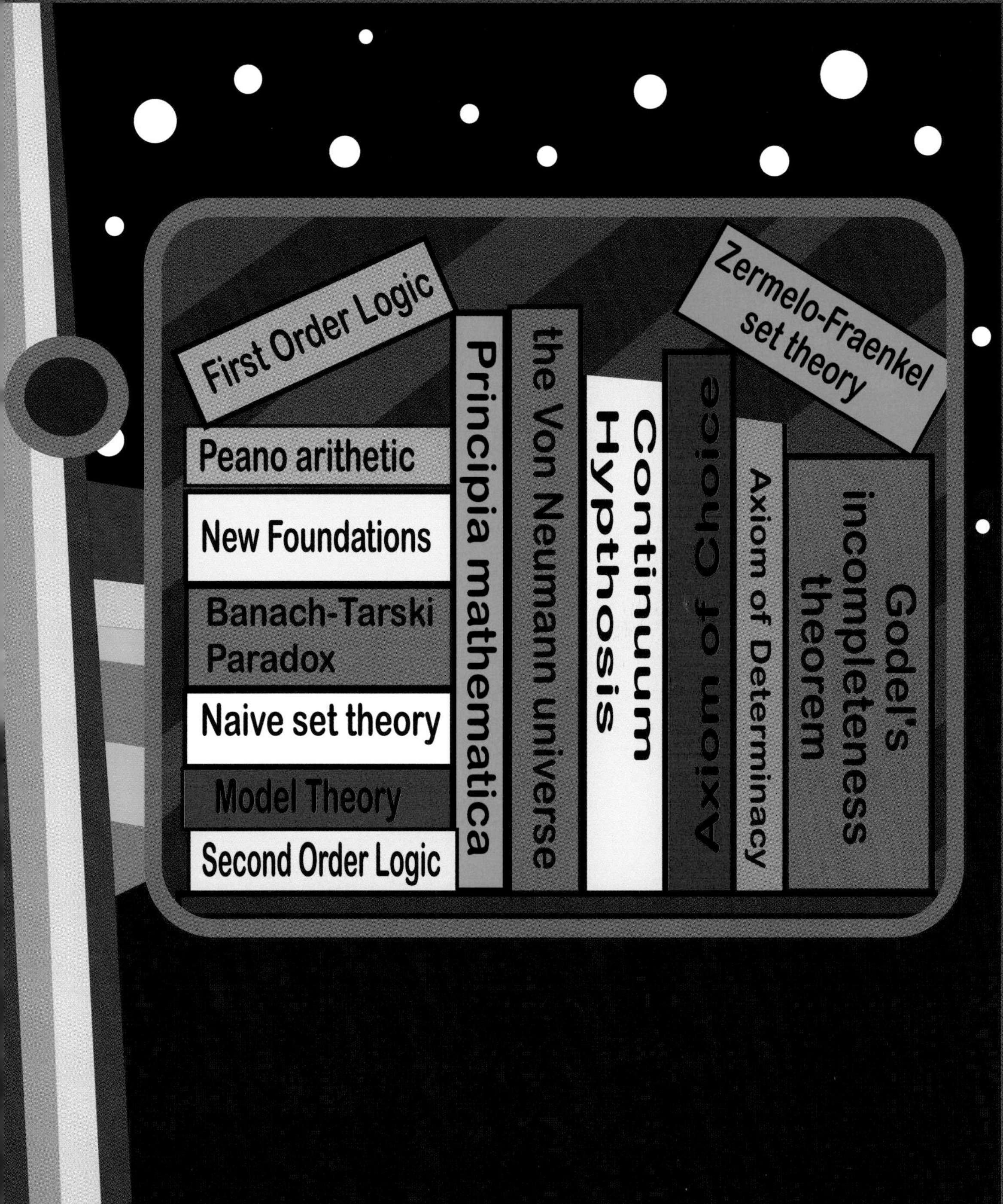

First Order Logic
Peano arithetic
New Foundations
Banach-Tarski Paradox
Naive set theory
Model Theory
Second Order Logic
Principia mathematica
the Von Neumann universe
Continuum Hypthosis
Axiom of Choice
Axiom of Determinacy
Godel's incompleteness theorem
Zermelo-Fraenkel set theory

this result follows logically from commonly accepted axioms of set theory, such as the Zermelo-Fraenkel axioms.

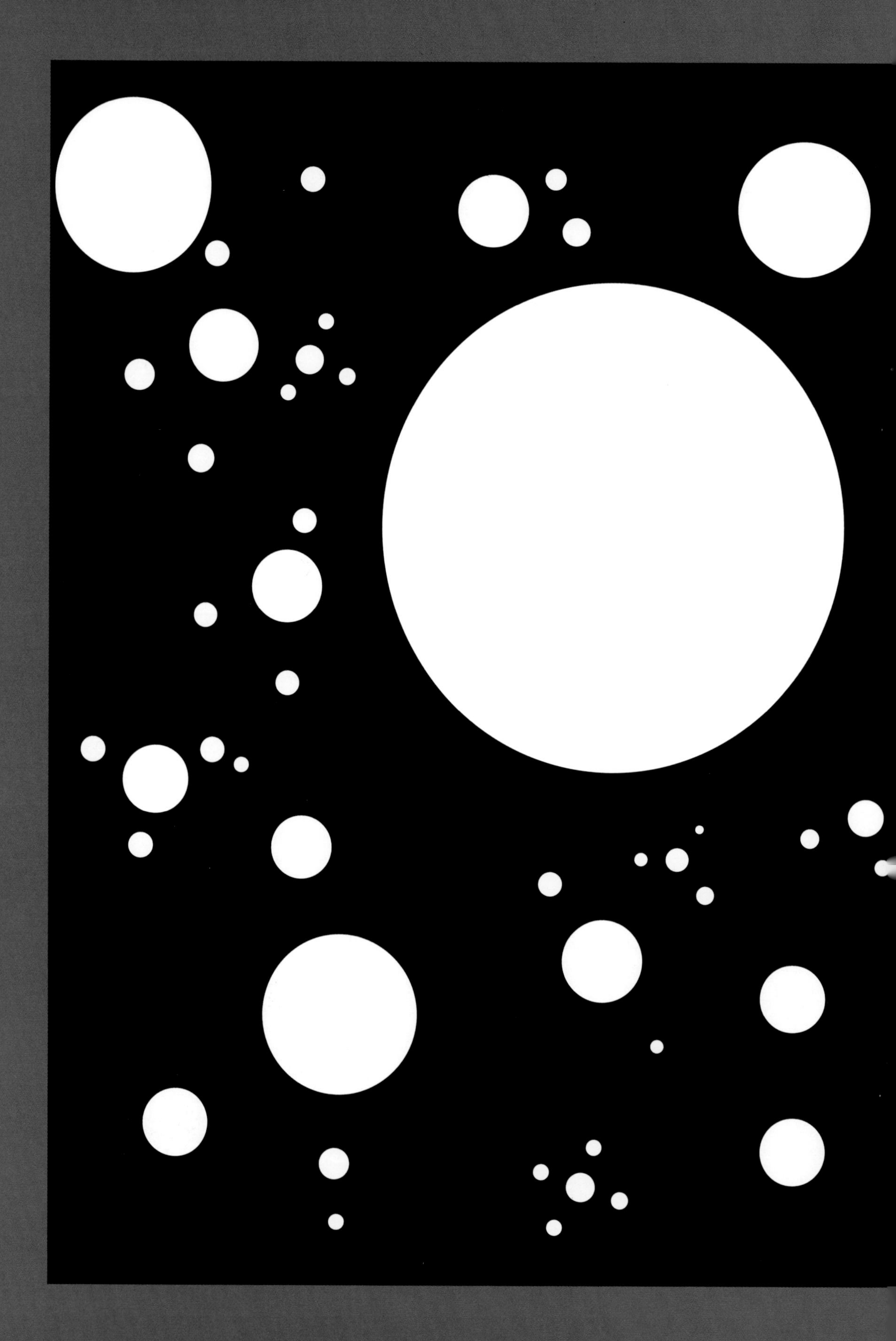

But, informally speaking,
I think that ....

infinity is
everywhere
we look.

Thanks:

I thank Brienne Brown, Tom Costa, Diana Davis, Peter Doyle, David Epstein, Dmitry Feldman, Sergei Gelfand, Eriko Hironaka, James Key, Masha Ryskin, Joshua Schechter, Lilith Schwartz, and Lucina Schwartz for their help with this book. I also thank the National Science Foundation for their support.

About the book:

I drew the pictures in this book using Inkscape.

About the author:

I am the Chancellor's Professor of Mathematics at Brown University. In my spare time I enjoy writing computer programs, listening to music, drawning cartoonish pictures, and thinking about geometry.